I Can Read!
I Can Write!

Creating a Print-Rich Environment

Written by Terri Beeler
Edited by Janet Bruno
Illustrated by Patty Briles

Winter Words

Snow
Snowman
Freeze
Icicle
Ski
Sled

The Three Billy Goats Gruff

I fed the rabbit...
Oct. 3 Jane
Oct. 4 chris
Oct. 5 Eduardo
Oct. 6 Brooke

What did YOU do this weekend?

I saw a movie. Sam
We went shopping Tami
MY grandma came over. Pedro
Mom and I baked cookies. Alice

What do Butterflies Eat?

Beautiful Butterflies

CTP © 1993, Creative Teaching Press, Inc., Cypress, CA 90630

Table of Contents

Table of Contents

4 Dramatic Play *Plus* Print

5 Getting Parents Involved

6 Resources

To the Teacher

The creation of a print-rich environment is an essential first step in the development of successful young readers and writers. Such an environment reinforces skills which have already begun to emerge as a result of exposure to reading and writing activities at home and to the uses of print in the child's environment.

During the last ten years we have learned a great deal about how children learn to read and write. Much has changed in the field we now refer to as "emergent literacy," even down to the way in which research is being conducted. How children learn to read and write is being studied in home and classroom situations, rather than in the laboratory. Conclusions are based on observations of children in learning situations, rather than on test results.

mi DINSR

Nicki

In *Literacy Development in the Early Years*, Lesley Mandel Morrow lists conclusions based on the results of current research. These conclusions have important implications for the classroom:

1 The development of literacy skills begins in infancy.

2 Parents play an important role in the development of these skills when they provide an environment rich in print and literacy activities.

3 Even very young children come to school with a knowledge of oral and written language.

4 Teachers must take responsibility for providing a print-rich environment which will continue to stimulate emerging literacy skills.

5 An environment which supports the emergence of literacy nurtures the development of a positive self-concept.

6 Both parents and teachers must be literacy models for children, demonstrating through daily activities the many uses of print.

7 The emergence of literacy requires social interaction with adults and other children.

8 Literacy experiences must be meaningful and **actively** involve the child.

I Can Read! I Can Write! presents easy-to-implement ways to apply this research. Take a few moments to look through the book and learn more about creating a print-rich environment. Find out how rewarding it can be to feature print in your classroom. You'll soon be pointing to students with pride, saying, "Look what he can read! Look what she can write!"

MARBLE ⋅ PAINTING

1. Put a sheet of paper in box.
2. Add 5 drops of paint.
3. Add 5 marbles.
4. Roll marbles in the box.

paper

Marbles

BOX

EXIT

RR

ONE WAY

Block Center

Castles

Castle

I Can Read! I Can Write!

How Do I Create a Print-Rich Environment?

 ## What is meant by the term "print-rich environment?"

In this case, the term "print-rich environment" refers to a classroom in which different kinds of print are abundantly displayed. Such a classroom contains all kinds of books and writing materials; prominently displayed lists, charts, labels, and signs; samples of student and adult writing; and materials that encourage students to use the written language at play. The teacher in a print-rich classroom uses print in a variety of contexts throughout the day, incorporating it in daily activities and routines and using it as a management tool. The teacher knows that a print-rich environment is a major factor in supporting the literacy development of young children.

 ## Should I have a reading/writing center or should reading/writing materials be in all centers?

Why not both? A literacy center provides a place where students can experience activities that are specifically designed to encourage the development of literacy skills. Some children need this extra focus to get them interested in reading and writing. A typical literacy center would include a library corner and a writing center, plus other language arts materials (puppets, listening post, flannel board, etc). To emphasize its importance, the literacy center should be large, accessible, and highly visible.

You can also provide numerous opportunities to read and write in other centers throughout the classroom. Stock your science, math, music, art, dramatic play, and block centers with books and writing materials. Post charts, maps, signs, and lists and see how various disciplines reinforce the language arts. When "doctors" at the dramatic play center write prescriptions or students at the science center record the growth of a plant, they are developing literacy skills.

 ## What should my library corner look like?

A well-designed library corner significantly increases the number of children who choose to participate in literacy activities. It should be a focal point of the classroom inviting children to come and read.

The library corner is a well-defined area of the classroom that provides privacy, yet can easily be supervised by the teacher. Several children should be able to use the library corner at one time.

A well-designed library corner includes such features as:

✓ A large variety of books

✓ Traditional bookshelves

✓ Open-faced bookshelves

✓ A system for checking out and shelving books such as the one described on page 38

✓ A variety of comfortable seating areas (rocking chair, beanbag chair, easy chair, large pillows, rug)

✓ Table and chairs

✓ A private spot such as a large, decorated appliance box, a teepee, or a table covered with a sheet

✓ Posters relating to reading and literature

✓ Stuffed animals for children to read to

✓ Flannel board and props for particular books

✓ Puppets (finger, stick, hand)

✓ Tape player, headsets, and cassettes to accompany favorite books

✓ Materials for writing

✓ Story props bagged together with a featured book to encourage story retellings

Library Corner

 ## What kinds of books do children need?

All kinds of books should be available in the classroom, including a wide variety of genres:

- concept books
- number books
- picture books
- wordless books
- informational books
- alphabet books
- predictable books
- books on social issues

- poetry
- nursery rhymes
- fairy tales
- folktales
- fables
- drama
- biographies
- mysteries

To meet the needs of all children, the books should represent a range of difficulty. As a general rule, provide five to eight books for every child. Since children often enjoy reading the same book a friend is reading, it's desirable to stock multiple copies of some books. Inexpensive books are available at garage sales, flea markets, and through children's book clubs. Also, parents and businesses are often willing to make donations to the class library.

Divide your book collection so that you can alternate the books every few weeks. New books will pique children's interest, and old favorites will be awaited with anticipation.

I Can Read! I Can Write!

How should I display books so children will use them?

Books should be visible throughout the room, with the greatest number and variety in the library corner. Place books on current topics of interest in other centers and learning areas. For example, books on frogs and toads could be placed in the science center next to an aquarium with tadpoles. Set up a separate area where children can display books from home that they want to share with their friends.

Keeping in mind that children are authors too, give them time, materials, and space to display books they have written. Children love to read books their classmates have written, and student authors are encouraged and validated by the interest in their books.

Books displayed with the front cover showing will catch a child's eye and encourage involvement in literature. Books stacked or shelved are not visually or physically accessible. They do not say "come and read." If you do not have room to store all of your books on open-faced shelving, feature a few different books each week.

Further stimulate children's interest in books by displaying them with materials that will enhance the reading experience:

- puppets and puppet theater
- flannel board
- read-a-long books and tapes
- writing and drawing materials
- stuffed animal "reading buddies"
- holiday or seasonal items
- items that reflect the topic of the book (pair books on insects with an insect collection)

What should my writing center look like?

The writing center is another component of the classroom literacy center. Furnish it with a table and chairs, plus lap boards for students who prefer to stretch out on the rug. Stock it with a wide variety of materials which invite children to explore writing in many forms. An extensive list of writing center materials is provided on page 13. The number and type of materials offered at the writing center will depend on the age of your students.

You can also suggest specific writing activities that reflect classroom events, such as writing responses to books read, making holiday cards, listing items for a cooking project, or writing questions to ask a guest speaker.

Writing Center Materials

Writing Tools

- Assorted pencils
- Colored pencils
- Crayons
- Colored chalk
- Ballpoint pens with a variety of ink colors
- Markers with different colors and tip sizes
- Erasers

Writing Materials

- Paper of all kinds and sizes (lined, unlined, colored and white)
- Envelopes
- "Stamps"
- Sticky notes (several sizes)
- Index cards (lined, unlined several sizes)
- Blank books
- Invitations
- Stationery
- Note pads (various sizes)
- Carbon paper
- Book making materials
- Tape, scissors, erasers, stapler, paper clips, hole punch

Writing Resources

- Books of all kinds
- Phone books
- Dictionary
- Menus
- Posters
- Map
- Globe
- Writing Wall (See p. 28)
- Calendars
- Newspapers
- Comic books
- Old magazines
- Children's magazines
- View Master
- Catalogs
- Alphabet chart
- Bulletin board to display writing
- Teacher-made books
- Story-starter cards

Writing Without Pencil and Paper

- Easel and paint
- Computer and paper
- Typewriter and paper
- Sandpaper letters
- Puff paint for tactile writing
- Flannel board/felt letters
- Magnetic letters
- Wooden letters
- Sand tub for "finger writing"
- Stencils (letter and picture)
- Rubber stamps/stamp pads
- Shaving cream used on table, cookie sheet, or tray for "finger writing"
- Magic slate
- Cookie cutter alphabet
- Playdough
- Pasta letters
- White laminate wipe-off board
- Chalkboards (individual and wall mounted)
- Tape recorder to record children's dictated stories

"Let's Pretend" Writing

- Old checks
- Message pads
- Appointment pads
- Entry blanks/junk mail
- Office forms
- Address books
- Order blanks
- Job applications

Getting Organized

- Individual student mailboxes (See p. 45)
- File folders accessible to children and clearly labeled with each child's name

❖ How should print be displayed?

Print should be displayed in a variety of ways depending upon the purpose of the display. If the purpose is to provide students with information, the display should be clear, uncluttered, and posted at a child's eye level. The focus should be on the print, and decoration should be kept to a minimum.

These readable displays may be the work of children or adults and should be evident in all learning areas. Some examples would be: a chart showing students how to perform a science experiment, a sign-up sheet for the computer, labels on classroom materials, a sign announcing a school assembly, directions for using the tape recorder, a student book review, the class calendar, and words to a song posted at the music center.

Sometimes the purpose for the display is to show off student writing pieces. Children feel validated as writers when their work is displayed for all to enjoy. They also become more aware of writing as a form of communication and personal expression. Papers should be dated and changed frequently to maintain students' interest. Be sure to reserve some space for students to display work of **their** choice.

What Can Magnets Pick Up?

Try each one.

Put them under yes or no.

Yes	No

Tell a friend what you found.

YES / NO Leaf

? Where should print be displayed?

Use your imagination to select display locations. Print can be displayed on bulletin boards, walls, doors, cabinets, windows, shelves; hanging from the ceiling; and even strung across the room on a clothesline. The only limitations are the physical features of your classroom and the purpose of the display.

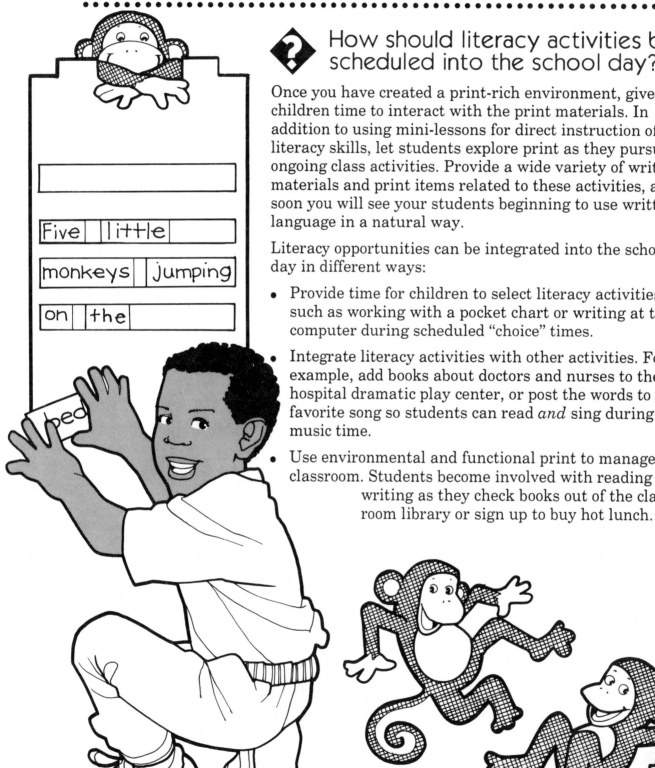

How should literacy activities be scheduled into the school day?

Once you have created a print-rich environment, give children time to interact with the print materials. In addition to using mini-lessons for direct instruction of literacy skills, let students explore print as they pursue ongoing class activities. Provide a wide variety of writing materials and print items related to these activities, and soon you will see your students beginning to use written language in a natural way.

Literacy opportunities can be integrated into the school day in different ways:

- Provide time for children to select literacy activities such as working with a pocket chart or writing at the computer during scheduled "choice" times.

- Integrate literacy activities with other activities. For example, add books about doctors and nurses to the hospital dramatic play center, or post the words to a favorite song so students can read *and* sing during music time.

- Use environmental and functional print to manage the classroom. Students become involved with reading and writing as they check books out of the classroom library or sign up to buy hot lunch.

? What is the teacher's role in a print-rich environment?

The teacher's role in a print-rich environment is varied and complex. An instructor of literacy skills and a facilitator in their development, the teacher provides children with a wide array of materials and many opportunities to learn and grow.

The teacher in a print-rich environment:

- Provides time and varied opportunities for literacy activities.

- Models reading and writing for students in his or her own daily routine.

- Plans the environment to encourage children's interactions with reading and writing and with other students.

- Uses reading and writing as essential elements in managing daily classroom routines.

- Introduces children to a wide variety of books.

- Listens to children read and reads to them daily.

- Listens to students' stories and helps students record them.

- Arranges print displays that are current and at the child's eye level.

- Observes the children's use of the environment to be sure that it is supporting their developing literacy.

- Understands that providing an environment supportive of a child's developing literacy is a way of thinking. It is not a teaching technique to be carried out in one specific way.

The Oreo® Cookies package is used with the permission of Nabisco, Inc.

Betty Crocker® is a registered trademark of General Mills, Inc., used with permission.

Environmental Print

 ## What is it?

- It's the print we see all around us—the print in our environment.

- It's the print on commercial signs, billboards, and labels of all kinds and the logos of the products we use every day.

- It's the print we recognize not so much because of the letters or words, but because of the colors, pictures, and shapes surrounding the print.

- It's the first print a child recognizes as literacy skills begin to emerge.

 ## Why should I use environmental print in my classroom?

- Children can often read environmental print in context, surrounded by familiar shapes, colors, and pictures.

- Children can feel successful "reading" at an early age.

- This early success motivates young children to read more and more!

 ## But is this really reading?

- It is an initial stage of reading.

- When children have become skilled at recognizing environmental print, they will move on to reading the words in the same form but without the color. Later they will be able to read the print in different contexts.

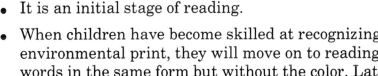

Swiss Miss® is reprinted with permission of Hunt Wesson, Inc.

Betty Crocker®, Super Moist®, and Nature Valley® are registered trademarks of General Mills, Inc., used with permission.

 ### What are some examples of environmental print that children might recognize?

The environmental print that a child recognizes depends on the child's life experiences. Some typical examples might be:

- The stop sign at the corner
- The sign on a neighborhood gas station or grocery store
- The wrapper on a child's favorite candy bar
- The box of a child's favorite cereal
- The label on a jar of peanut butter
- The "exit" sign above a door
- The sign for a child's favorite fast food restaurant
- The name on a tube of toothpaste

And lots, lots more! The possibilities are endless!

 ### How can I introduce the use of environmental print in my classroom?

Ask students to start collecting samples of environmental print to bring to school. (See parent letter on collecting environmental print, p. 69.) Provide each child with a special place, such as a folder, to save the samples. Use these samples for the student activities described on pages 21-28 in this chapter.

Remember these tips for using environmental print:

★ The print that each child can "read" depends on his environment and experiences.

★ Environmental print should be used in as full a context as possible, surrounded by familiar colors, pictures, and shapes.

★ When you remove the color from the print by making black and white copies, you change the context. This should be done only with more advanced children.

Environmental Print Scrapbooks

Procedure

▲ Children collect samples of environmental print to bring to school.

▲ When children are able to read their samples, they can begin to publish individual books of their own environmental print. Mount print samples in/on:

- Magnetic scrapbooks
- Spiral notebooks
- Construction paper books assembled by the child
- Three-ring binders
- Accordion books

Possible Uses

▲ Put the scrapbooks at centers for children to share and enjoy.

▲ During circle time, choose a Reader for the Day to share his or her book.

▲ Have children find matching samples in their classmates' books.

▲ Have children identify various fast foods, cereals, toothpastes, traffic signs, etc.

▲ Save one scrapbook for each student's assessment portfolio.

▲ As an ongoing project, have students collect an environmental print sample for every letter of the alphabet. Staple the pages together to make a personal ABC Book.

▲ Have children bring duplicate samples of print for class books, such as "Our Favorite Foods," "Favorite Places to Eat," or "Signs We See."

"I Can Read" Bags

Procedure

▲ Children collect samples of environmental print to bring to school. (See letter to parents on collecting environmental print, p. 69.)

▲ Give each child an "I Can Read" Bag for their print samples. This bag can be a brown, white, or colored lunch bag or a special gift bag. (Gift bags with handles are especially nice.) Each child decorates his own bag and writes his name and the words "I Can Read" on the outside.

▲ Designate an accessible place to store the bags.

Possible Uses

▲ Encourage children to share their print samples with a classmate during center time. Guide children by talking about where the sample comes from and what it has in common with the other child's samples. For example, "Tommy, tell me about this sample. Where did you get this candy label? John, do you have any candy labels?"

▲ When a child demonstrates that he can read his samples, let him post them on a special display board. Set aside a space for each child, and title the board "I Can Read."

Peter Pan® Peanut Butter is reprinted with permission of Hunt Wesson, Inc.

Environmental Print Puzzles

Procedure

▲ Have children bring in prepared food boxes such as cereals, cake mixes, and crackers. If possible, children should bring duplicate samples.

▲ Cut the front of one box into pieces to make a puzzle. For young children, the second box can serve as a guide to assembling the puzzle. The box or a self-sealing plastic bag can be used to store the puzzle.

Possible Uses

▲ Children can piece together and read a puzzle made from their own print sample.

▲ Children can share puzzles and experiences connected with the product. For example, "This says *Crest*®. That's my toothpaste. I use it every morning so I won't get cavities."

▲ A larger puzzle can be created by making a collage of samples on a piece of tagboard and then cutting the tagboard into pieces.

Betty Crocker® is registered trademark of General Mills, Inc., used with permission.

Concentration

Environmental print samples can be used to create matching games like Concentration, Tic-Tac-Toe, and Lotto. The newspaper is usually full of colorful coupons which can be used for these games.

How to Make

▲ Collect 5 to 10 matching pairs of print samples. (The number depends on the age of the children. You will want more for an older child.)

▲ All samples used to construct the game should be familiar to most children. Samples should not be included unless they have already been introduced to the class.

▲ Mount each sample on a piece of tagboard. All tagboard pieces should be the same size.

How to Play

▲ Concentration can be played by one student or a small group of 2-4 children. Players turn all of the samples face down so the print cannot be seen.

▲ The first player turns over two print samples at a time trying to find a matching pair. If successful, the player keeps the pair and takes another turn. When an unmatched pair is turned over, a different player takes a turn.

▲ Children try to read each sample they turn over. Classmates may help.

▲ The game can consist of pieces in a particular category, such as cereals or traffic logos.

▲ Children can also sort and classify the game cards by type (all the cereals, candies, or toys).

Swiss Miss® is reprinted with permission of Hunt Wesson, Inc.

I Can Read! I Can Write! Creative Teaching Press

Tic-Tac-Toe

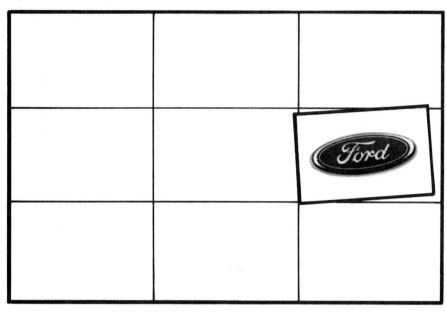

How to Make

▲ Construct Tic-Tac-Toe boards from tagboard, dividing the board into 9 equal squares or boxes. When deciding on the size of the game board and squares, consider the size of the print samples. Include as much of the print context as possible.

▲ Using duplicate print samples, make 2 sets of 5 matching game pieces. For example, one child might use 5 McDonald's® labels and the other player might use 5 Cheerio® labels. Remember not to use black and white copies of the samples because color provides an important context clue.

▲ To increase students' exposure to different print, make several different sets of game pieces.

How to Play

▲ Model how to play Tic-Tac-Toe. The winner is the first player to get three matching pieces in a horizontal, vertical, or diagonal line.

▲ Some strategies may be taught to older children.

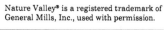

Nature Valley® is a registered trademark of
General Mills, Inc., used with permission.

Print Lotto

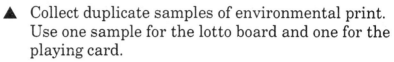

How to Make

▲ Collect duplicate samples of environmental print. Use one sample for the lotto board and one for the playing card.

▲ Construct lotto boards from tagboard, dividing the board into 9 equal squares or boxes. When deciding on the size of the game board and squares, consider the size of the print samples. Include as much context as possible. Every square on every board will have a different print sample.

▲ Make 9 playing cards for each player. For example, if 4 children will be playing the game, make 36 playing cards. The cards should match the print samples on the boards.

How to Play

▲ Give each player a lotto board and put all lotto cards face down in the center of the play area. Each child takes a turn, drawing a card and reading the print without showing other players the print sample.

▲ Older children read the samples on their boards to find out if they can match the card. (Younger students use visual clues.)

▲ The child who has the sample on his game board gets the card and places it on his board. If no one has the sample, the card goes onto a discard pile.

▲ The player covering his game board first, wins!

Variations

For very young children, players show each card to allow visual matching.

Use cards for sorting and classifying by type of item.

The Oreo® Cookies package is used with the permission of Nabisco, Inc.
Peter Pan® Peanut Butter is reprinted with permission of Hunt Wesson, Inc.
Nature Valley® is a registered trademark of General Mills, Inc., used with permission.

Additional Suggestions for Using Environmental Print

Bulletin Boards

Many different kinds of bulletin boards can be created using environmental print samples:

▲ **Can You Read This?** In a small display space, post a different sample each day. Children try to identify the print and draw a picture showing where the label might be found.

▲ **I Can Read!** Children make a collage display of environmental print samples they can read. New samples can be added throughout the year. Samples can also be categorized and labeled appropriately. Then the bulletin board becomes a great source of information for graphing activities.

▲ **My Favorite _____** Focus on a particular kind of environmental print (signs, soup labels, cereals) for a specified length of time. Encourage children to bring samples of the same kind to post on the board.

Writing Wall

▲ Post a very large piece of white butcher paper on the wall and place crayons nearby. Then let children try to duplicate their favorite print samples. (Be sure they sign their drawings.) This makes a good free choice activity.

Using Coupons

▲ Coupons from the newspaper and advertising fliers can be used to make the games described in this section. Save extra samples and put them in centers for children to use for art activities, sorting and classifying, and buddy reading.

Environmental Print Board Game

▲ Make a simple game board such as the one shown. You will need tagboard, print samples, a spinner or dice, and a game marker for each player. Students practice reading the print samples and directions as they move along the path.

3 Functional Print

What is it?

- Functional print gives children a reason to read by providing information they need, such as information about routines, procedures, schedules, and assignments.

- It includes labels on learning materials and suggestions for activities posted around the room.

- It is print written by children to share information. (For example, a brief description of a show-and-tell item.)

- It is print which helps the teacher manage the class more efficiently, such as a Helper Chart or a sign-in sheet.

- Functional print sometimes asks for a response from a child. For example, it can be a sign-up chart next to an easel which says, *I Painted Today*.

But my students can't read . . .

- To convey meaning, functional print is often used in combination with pictures, symbols, and assorted materials. For example, after reading *Clifford, the Big Red Dog*, an independent cooking activity could be set up at the snack center. Each child would make a Clifford Salad (see page 43) by reading from a large rebus recipe card. All ingredients and utensils would be labeled.

And my students can't write . . .

- Functional print that asks for a written response from a child (such as the child's name, the name of a favorite book, the results of an activity) does not require conventional writing. Depending on the child's stage of development, "writing" can be pictures or scribbling. It is important to accept their approximations. The purpose is to develop an understanding that print is a way to communicate, just like talking.

Good Morning Message

A Daily Written Greeting

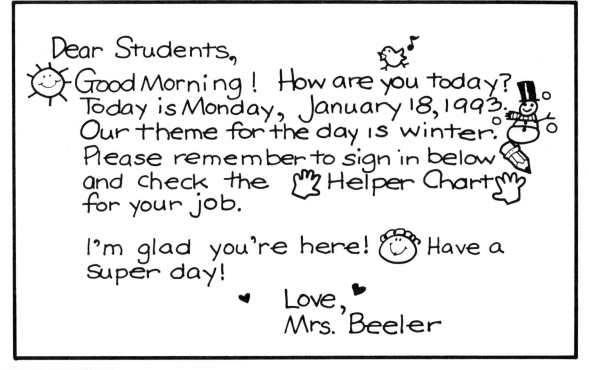

Dear Students,
Good Morning! How are you today?
Today is Monday, January 18, 1993.
Our theme for the day is winter.
Please remember to sign in below
and check the Helper Chart
for your job.

I'm glad you're here! Have a
super day!
                    Love,
                    Mrs. Beeler

Procedure

- The good morning message uses written language for instructions usually given orally. It should be written on lined chart paper or on the chalkboard and should be placed in the same location every day.

- Children should read it the first thing each morning. The class can also read the message out loud as a large group activity.

- If you keep the same basic wording, changing only a few words, such as the date, students will soon recognize the frequently used words.

- A sentence might be added to remind children of a special event or activity.

Additional Ideas

- Search for a specific sound, letter, or word in the message.

- Count the number of words in a specific sentence or in the message.

- Identify capitals, punctuation, etc. and discuss how they are used.

- Have one child each day write in day, date, and year.

- Write the message on word cards and place them in a pocket chart. Children arrange the cards to make sentences.

Who's at School Today?

Attendance Chart

Procedure

- Make a bulletin board, similar to the one shown above, that can be used as a daily attendance chart.

- Teach children to find their name tag as they come into class and move it from *home* to *school*.

- Put some other print items, such as a stop sign, along the road from home to school.

- Have children move their name tags from *school* to *home* when they leave for the day.

- The attendance board can also highlight themes, holidays, etc. However it is done, the focus should be on the print.

Additional ideas

- A pocket holding numbered index cards (one for each child in your class) can also be a part of the bulletin board. Make two additional pockets titled *How many are here today?* and *How many are absent today?* Children count the number of name tags *at home* and *at school* and place the correct number card in the correct pocket.

- For very young children, show each name tag individually, read it out loud, and have each child come up and place his tag *at school*.

- When children learn to recognize each other's names, appoint a daily attendance monitor to call out the names and place the tags *at school*.

It's Lunch Time

Lunch Chart

Procedure

- Post a lunch chart, such as the one shown, near the door of the classroom.

- The chart is made from a large (approximately 24" diameter) circle of tagboard divided into 4 sections.

- Label each section and add an appropriate picture to help children read the print. Possible labels:

  I brought my lunch.

  I'm buying my lunch.

  I'm buying milk.

  I'm buying ice cream.

- Clothespins are stored with the lunch chart as shown. Each clothespin has a child's name on it. Provide extra clothespins for students who may need to select two options. For example, the child who brings a lunch but also wants to buy milk needs two clothespins.

- As children come into class each day, they put their clothespins on the appropriate sections of the chart.

- This chart gives children an opportunity to use print to manage their environment. And it helps you make a quick daily lunch count.

Additional Ideas

- The day's menu may be posted with the chart so children can read what is being served.

- A graph can be posted next to the chart so the children can keep track of lunch preferences for the week or month.

Today Is . . .

Calendar

Procedure

- A calendar activity can become part of your everyday routine and may be done in conjunction with attendance.

- Post a large calendar like the one shown above near the location of your circle time activities. (Children will also use the calendar when they check out library books and when they date work or displays.)

- Review the name of the month and the day with the whole class. Then have the children count the days in the month to the current day and decide what comes next. As the children count, the Calendar Helper points to each day and puts up the new date.

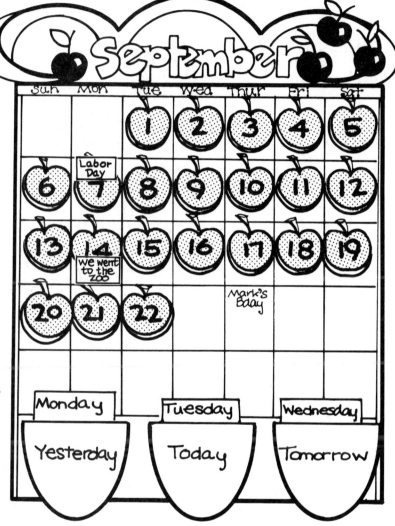

Additional Ideas

- Pockets with the words *Yesterday*, *Today*, and *Tomorrow* may be added to the calendar. Supply cards for each day of the week. The children can take turns placing the correct cards in each pocket.

- Mark holidays, special events, and birthdays on the calendar. Have children count the days to the special day and read the name of the day.

- At the end of the school day, group the children around the calendar and ask the Calendar Helper to mention one special thing about the day. The helper or the teacher then records this on the calendar. Review these items at the end of the month and graph the favorite activities.

The Weather Is . . .

Weather Chart

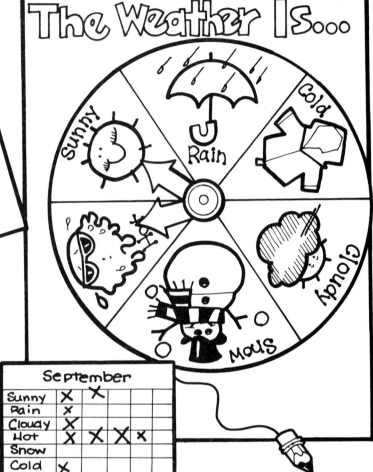

The Weather Is...

September						
Sunny	X	X				
Rain	X					
Cloudy	X					
Hot	X	X	X	x		
Snow						
Cold	X					

Procedure

- Post a weather chart like the one shown above next to the class calendar described on page 33. You will need to attach two or three tagboard arrows with a large paper fastener in the center of the chart.

- The chart should show words and pictures for various weather conditions: sunny, rainy, cold, cloudy, hot, foggy, snowy, overcast, windy. Be sure the print is visible.

- The Weather Helper decides what the day's weather is and chooses all the words that apply, such as *cold* and *rainy*. Move the pointers to the correct terms and read them aloud.

Additional Ideas

- Add a weather graph and fill it in every day.

- Add envelopes labeled with the name and picture of each type of weather. Put several weather poems in each envelope. The Weather Helper will choose a poem from the appropriate envelope for the teacher or class to read.

What Time Is It?

Daily Schedule

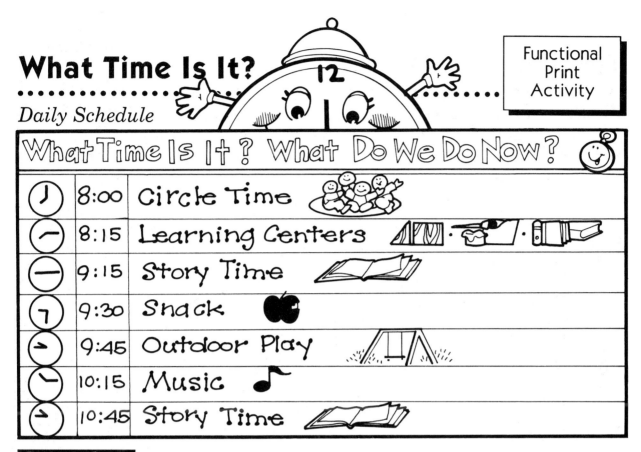

What Time Is It? What Do We Do Now?

🕐	8:00	Circle Time	
🕐	8:15	Learning Centers	
🕐	9:15	Story Time	
🕐	9:30	Snack	
🕐	9:45	Outdoor Play	
🕐	10:15	Music	
🕐	10:45	Story Time	

Procedure

- A daily schedule posted near the clock offers opportunities for the use of print and for informal work on time concepts.

- Printed on posterboard, the schedule lists each activity and what time it starts. The time is also shown on a traditional clock face.

- Where possible, there should be a picture of the activity that children can associate with the print.

- The schedule can be introduced at the beginning of the year during circle time. As activities change throughout the day, the teacher draws attention to the print, asking, "What is it time for us to do now?"

Additional Ideas

- The daily schedule can be set up in a pocket chart format, with the time and the activity on separate sentence strips. In this way, the teacher can change the activities and their times without redoing the entire chart.

- Appoint a daily Time Keeper who announces when it's time to clean up and start the next activity. Children who cannot tell time watch for the clock to match the clock faces on the schedule. The teacher tells the Time Keeper when the time is close so he does not spend all of his time watching the clock.

This Class Lends a Helping Hand

Helper Chart

Procedure

- A classroom helper chart provides many opportunities for using print. To encourage children to read the chart, include as many job titles as possible and change jobs frequently.

- The job chart lists the job in print and shows it in picture form. Jobs can include:
    - Line Leader
    - Line Ender (Caboose)
    - Light Helper
    - Door Monitor
    - Flag Salute Monitor
    - Snack Helper
    - Clean-Up Monitors (for each center)
    - Runner (takes notes to office)
    - Table Captains
    - Chalkboard Eraser
    - Library Monitor
    - Show-and-Tell Announcer
    - Calendar Helper
    - Weather Helper
    - Plant/Animal Caretaker
    - Equipment Monitor (balls, ropes)
    - Teacher Assistant (passes out papers, pencils, etc.)
    - Display Monitor (keeps displays current)
    - Story Time Leader (chooses the book to be read)

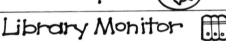

We're Lending a Helping Hand!

Light Helper	💡	Tim
Snack Helper	🍎	Lee
Plant Caretaker	🪴	Pat
Weatherman	☁️	Steve
Story Time Leader	📖	Liz
Calendar Keeper	📅	Philip
Zoo Keeper		Jo
Library Monitor	📚	Maria

- Make a laminated name card for each child. Helpers place their name cards next to the appropriate job title.

- To make sure all children get a turn at each job, keep a current record of which jobs students have held.

Additional Ideas

- To allow flexibility, the chart can be made of sentence strips inserted into a pocket chart.

- Next to the chart hang a notebook of job descriptions in rebus form. As jobs change, encourage children to review their job description.

We're on the Move!

Center Rotation

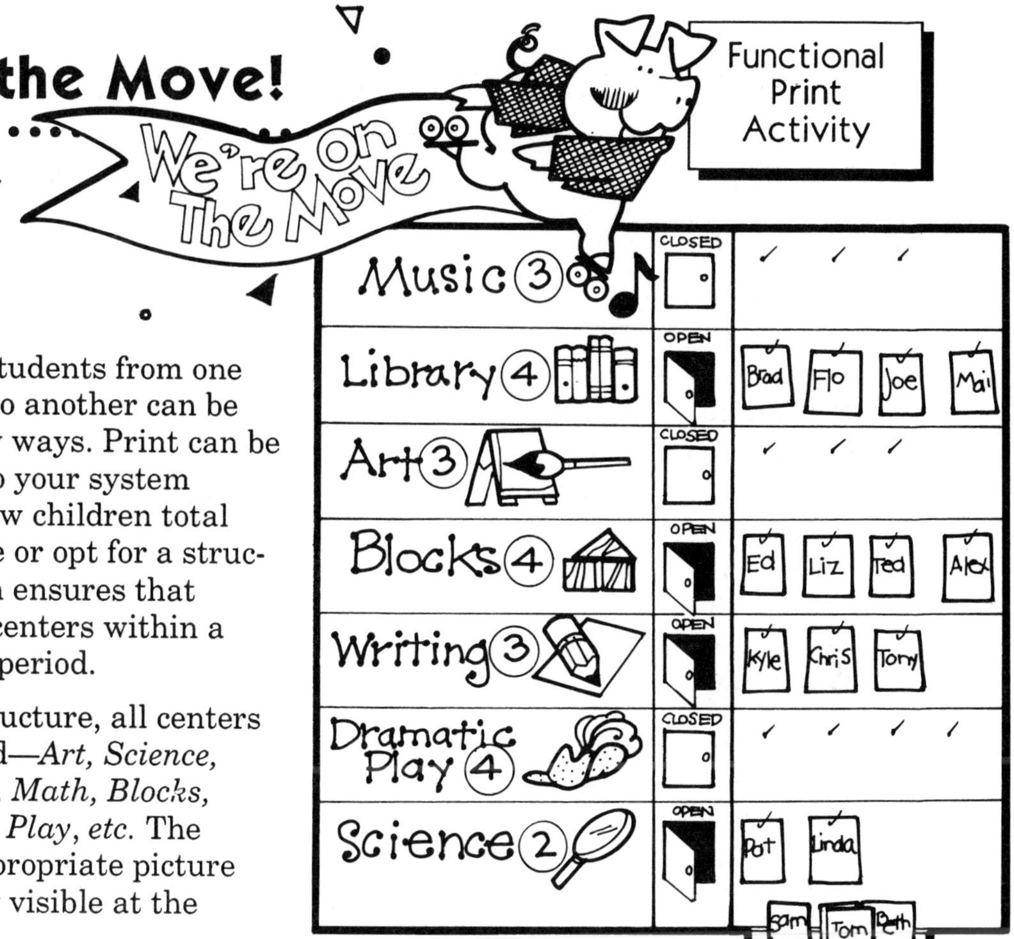

Procedure

- The rotation of students from one learning center to another can be handled in many ways. Print can be incorporated into your system whether you allow children total freedom of choice or opt for a structured plan which ensures that children use all centers within a designated time period.

- Regardless of structure, all centers should be labeled—*Art, Science, Writing, Library, Math, Blocks, Music, Dramatic Play,* etc. The name and an appropriate picture should be clearly visible at the center.

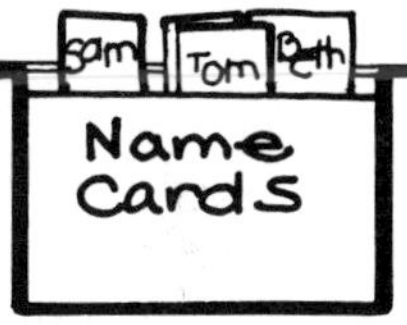

Music ③	CLOSED	✓ ✓ ✓
Library ④	OPEN	Brad · Flo · Joe · Mai
Art ③	CLOSED	✓ ✓ ✓
Blocks ④	OPEN	Ed · Liz · Ted · Alex
Writing ③	OPEN	Kyle · Chris · Tony
Dramatic Play ④	CLOSED	✓ ✓ ✓ ✓
Science ②	OPEN	Pat · Linda

Sam · Tom · Beth

Name Cards

- Post a chart, similar to the one illustrated above, showing the names of all centers and the number of children who may be in a particular center at a given time. This chart can be an interactive bulletin board, visible from anywhere in the room. During each center period, indicate on the chart the centers that are *open* for use.

- Either you or the children put their names next to the center name on the chart, and they proceed to the center. When students move from one center to another, they change the placement of their names.

Additional Ideas

- Place a folder for each child's work in a box next to the rotation chart. Each folder should contain a chart which the child fills out daily, indicating the centers where he has worked that day. This record can go home to parents on a weekly basis or be kept as part of the child's assessment portfolio.

- Keep clipboards at each center so children can sign in and out. This will give the children literacy practice and the teacher a record of center use.

We're Reading, Reading, Reading

Using the Classroom Library

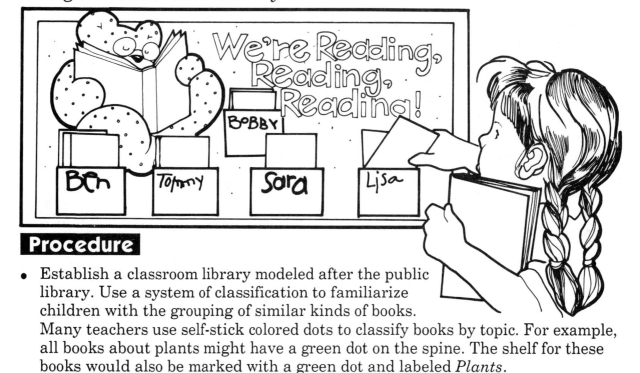

Procedure

- Establish a classroom library modeled after the public library. Use a system of classification to familiarize children with the grouping of similar kinds of books. Many teachers use self-stick colored dots to classify books by topic. For example, all books about plants might have a green dot on the spine. The shelf for these books would also be marked with a green dot and labeled *Plants*.

- Place a library pocket and an index card, with the title written on it, in each book.

- Put up a bulletin board with a library pocket for each child's name.

- When a child wants to take out a book, he checks the class calendar and writes the date on the title card. Then he puts the card in his own personal bulletin board pocket. When the book is returned, the return date is recorded on the card, and the card is placed back in the book. Finally, the child shelves the book in the proper place.

Additional Ideas

- You may want to keep track of the books each child reads to include in an assessment portfolio. This can be done in a number of ways. Here are two suggestions:

  1. Put an additional card in the child's pocket. When a book is returned, the date and title are written on this card also. In this way, the child develops a list of the titles he has read.

  2. Place a tab for each child on a separate page of a spiral notebook. Attach this notebook to the bulletin board so children can record the books they have read.

I Can Write My Name

Name Writing

Children quickly learn that print conveys information when they are given the opportunity to use their name in meaningful ways. Remember, young children participating in these types of activities may not be using conventional writing. It is important to accept their approximations. Here are some examples that will help children understand that print is a form of communication:

Procedure

- Put up a sign next to the art center titled *I Pasted Today*, leaving space for each child to sign their name as they complete the activity. This will show you who has participated. This type of sign-up can be used next to any center, classroom job, or special activity—*I Fed the Fish Today, I Watered the Plants, I Cooked Today.*

- A chart with *I Like Apples* at the top of one column and *I Like Bananas* at the top of another column gives children an opportunity to write their name and also provides information that can later be graphed. This type of simple chart can be used to record any kind of information—shoe color, hair color, favorite TV programs, favorite foods, etc.

- A large tagboard tooth saying *I Lost a Tooth* gives children an opportunity to write their names and also lets everyone else know about this very special event.

- Having children "sign in" each morning is a good extension to the attendance chart on page 31. Very young children can place a name card in an attendance box.

Who Will Show and Tell Today?

Show-and-Tell Chart

Procedure

- A show-and-tell chart allows students to participate in the management of classroom routines.

- The chart has five pockets, labeled Monday through Friday. Next to the display is a larger pocket holding a name card for each class member. A day or two before a child plans to bring something for sharing, he places his name card in the appropriate pocket.

- When it is time for sharing, the show-and-tell helper takes out the name cards and calls each child who is to share that day.

Additional Ideas

- After show and tell, encourage children to label and display their sharing items.

- If show and tell is done around assigned themes, leave a space on the chart for that theme.

- Give older children more print opportunities by adding a pocket with preprinted slips that say, *My show-and-tell day is _____. The theme for the week is _____.* When a child places his card in the pocket, he takes a slip and fills in the day of the week and the theme. This slip goes home to parents to remind them that their child should bring something for show and tell.

Congratulations, You're Special!

Recognition Displays

Procedure

- Plan a bulletin board that features one child each week. Possible titles are *You're a Star*, *I'm Somebody Special*, or *Student of the Week*. This type of recognition display gives a boost to a child's self-esteem and also provides one more opportunity for the use of print.

- The display might include: the child's name, a photograph, samples of the child's work, facts about the child (birthday, hobbies), a favorite book, items from home which are meaningful to the child.

- Appropriate labels can be written by the student or dictated to an adult.

Additional Ideas

- Make a bulletin board that highlights personal accomplishments of class members, such as learning how to tie shoes, skip, or count to 100.

- Feature one child's unique talents with a special display. For example, post newspaper clippings, program notes, and photos of Emily, a young ballerina. Add several brief statements about her dancing experiences to the display. Draw attention to these accomplishments during circle time.

We're Going on a Trip

Field Trips

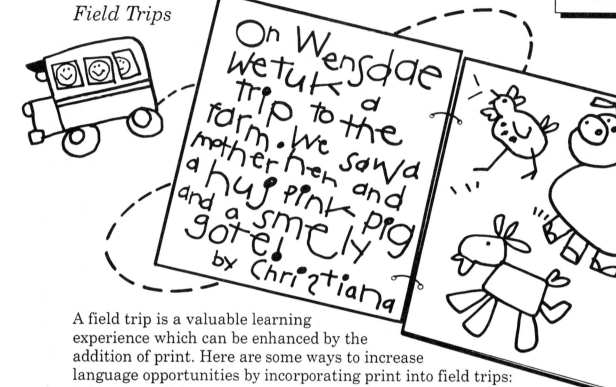

On Wensdae we tuk a trip to the farm. We sawa a mother hen and a huj pink pig and a smely gotel
by Christiana

A field trip is a valuable learning experience which can be enhanced by the addition of print. Here are some ways to increase language opportunities by incorporating print into field trips:

Procedure

- Before the field trip, read aloud books related to the trip and have books available for students to enjoy on their own.

- Talk to the children about the trip. Have them dictate a list of the things they expect to see.

- Make a chart featuring new vocabulary related to the trip.

- With the children's help, write a schedule for the trip listing trip activities, departure time, and return time.

- Read the permission slip with the children. Design the slip so there is a place for children to sign their name above the parent's signature.

- Working with the children, trace the route you will take on a city map.

- After returning to school, talk with the children about what they saw. Have them write, dictate, and/or illustrate stories about the trip to display on a bulletin board. Save these for student assessment portfolios.

- As a class or individually, write thank-you notes to a contact person at the field trip site.

Now We're Cooking

Classroom Cooking

Classroom cooking activities provide many enjoyable opportunities for exploring print.

Procedure

- The recipe should be written in rebus format on large posterboard or chart paper, with a pictorial representation of each ingredient and the quantity to be used. (See page 77 for a list of classroom cookbooks.) All ingredients and utensils should be labeled.

Clifford Salad

1. Put 1 Pear half on the plate.
2. Add 2 Apple Slices for ears.
3. Put on 2 Raisins for eyes.
4. Put on 1 Cherry nose.

Say "Hi" to Clifford!

- Make a cooking vocabulary chart that includes words like *measure, mix, stir, sift, spread, grate*. Add new words as they come up and review the old ones frequently.

- Post a list of safety rules and discuss the ones relevant to the current recipe.

- Post a list of clean-up jobs and assign children to see that they are done.

Additional Ideas

- Encourage children to write a story about their cooking experiences.

- Keep a class cookbook with one recipe to a page. Let children illustrate this book titled *Now We're Cooking*.

- Make cooking a literature extension activity. For example, after reading *Goldilocks and the Three Bears*, children make porridge.

Words, Words, and More Words

Personal Word Banks

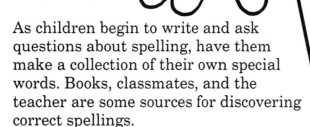

As children begin to write and ask questions about spelling, have them make a collection of their own special words. Books, classmates, and the teacher are some sources for discovering correct spellings.

Procedure

- Have each child make a book with a title such as *My Very Own Words*. As students ask for and discover the correct spellings of words that interest them, they record and illustrate the words in their own personal dictionaries.

- Keep a dictionary, a box of index cards, and a pencil in a special place. As children find new words, they make new word cards. Each child should have a storage place at their desk: a self-sealing bag, cigar box, or card file.

- Cover a wall with butcher paper and title it *These Are Our Words!* As children learn new words, they write them on the wall. When a child wants to know the spelling of a word, he can look on the wall.

- Plan a time for students to share their new words with classmates. Children love to have a chance to show off the new words they have learned.

- Introduce a "Word of the Day" related to a current theme unit. Students can add the word to their dictionaries or word boxes. Encourage them to use the word throughout the day and to look for it in other contexts.

I've Got a Letter

Student Mailboxes

Room 5 Post Office

Mark · Mark · Tomás · LaQuista · Pam · Aaron · Jenny · BEN · Samantha · Chris

Procedure

- Make mailboxes for yourself and for each child in the class. Label each mailbox with a student's name. The following materials make satisfactory classroom mailboxes. Some will need to be covered with paint, construction paper, or Con-Tact™ paper.

    Shoe boxes
    Half-gallon milk cartons
    l-lb. coffee cans
    Colorful file folders
    Commercial cardboard shoe organizers or hanging plastic shoe bag
    Cereal boxes or large envelopes stapled on a bulletin board
    Lunch bags taped to desks

- To encourage letter writing, put pencils, paper, and other letter writing materials near the post office.

- Tips for using mailboxes:

    - Encourage children to write at least one message a day.

    - Let children know that you like to receive letters.

    - Talk to children about the courtesy of replying promptly to someone who writes them a letter.

    - Have one child be the mail carrier for the day or week.

    - Consider assigning pen pals so everyone will be involved in writing and receiving letters.

    - Encourage very young children to write by accepting writing approximations such as drawing and scribbling.

Do YOU Have a Letter?

Alex · Andrea · Grace · Matt · Robbie · Stephen

Notes From the Teacher

Teacher-Modeled Writing

Dear Pam,
    You really seemed to enjoy that book by Tomie de Paola. Maybe we can find another of his books in the library.

        Mrs. Beeler

Procedure

- It is very important for the teacher to frequently model the use of writing. This can be done through "quickie messages" which boost self-esteem and develop an understanding of the uses of print.

- Every day look and listen for message material. Keep a note pad close by at all times. Commercial awards are fine for special occasions, but for everyday use a simple note pad will do.

Sample messages:

✎ *One child helps another child complete an activity:* "It made me feel good when I saw you helping Tommy. Thank you."

✎ *A child tells you about something that happened at home*: "It must have been really scary when you saw the smoke coming from the kitchen. You were really brave. Thanks for telling me your story."

✎ *A special show-and-tell item:* "It was fun to see your book from the circus. It sounds like you had a very good time."

✎ *A child's new clothes or haircut:* "You look especially pretty today. I like your new red dress."

✎ *An activity a child has shown particular interest in:* "You really seemed to enjoy our art activity today! Maybe we can do it again another time."

What's in a Name?

Labeling

Class Bear

Class Bear

Procedure

- Many teachers of young children label every object in the room — clock, desk, table, sink, etc. Some researchers now question whether this kind of one-word label really serves a purpose. Here are some ways to give labels a purpose and increase their value:

  - ✎ Make a game using the labels. Read aloud the labels you have placed around the room, then have students read the labels to you (individually or as a group).

  - ✎ Give children cards to match with the labels in the room. These cards can be kept in a bucket for individual use during center time.

  - ✎ In addition to the set of label cards, make a matching set of picture cards. Show children how to match the label cards with the picture cards. These two sets can also be used to play Concentration. (See p. 24.)

  - ✎ Use complete sentences in labeling: *This is a table. You may sit at the table.* This label provides more information and tells the item's purpose. It also gives children more experience with conventional uses of print.

- Displays and activities are often labeled by teachers and students. For instance, a child might put his name on a show-and-tell item or write a descriptive label for a school project. The teacher might put the following label next to the hamster cage: *This is Harriet, our pet hamster. Feed her hamster food and fresh water every day.*

- To encourage children to participate in this use of print, materials for labeling should be available throughout the classroom.

I Can Read! I Can Write!

4 Dramatic Play *Plus* Print

? Why add print to dramatic play?

Dramatic play, long recognized as an important part of child's play, encourages the development of social skills and problem solving skills. It also promotes an understanding of "real world" roles. When you add print, you increase the value of dramatic play and remind children that literacy skills are important in the real world. Think of all the "real life" activities that children participate in through dramatic play and the importance of reading and writing in these activities. Reading and writing are a part of almost everything we do!

? How do I get my children to use print in their dramatic play?

- As children are playing, make suggestions, such as "Let's make a list for grocery shopping." Or, "Why don't you write down what Susie wants to eat?" Get children accustomed to using print while playing. Children may even ask for materials to do the things they have seen done in real life settings.

- The next step is to add various forms of print to a center, **a few at a time.** Suggest uses for the print or let children discover uses on their own. For example, if an airplane has been set up, supply paper and pencil so students can take drink orders from passengers. Provide baggage tags, tickets, pens, and pencils so they can check in passengers. Signs giving various instructions can also be posted.

- A play situation which is familiar to children can be very motivating. So, whenever possible, set up your own version of favorite places in the community, such as fast food restaurants, markets, or clothing stores. These businesses are usually happy to donate items bearing their logo.

- Use the specific suggestions on pages 52-65 in this chapter to integrate print into dramatic play activities.

What is my role in dramatic play?

- Teachers should not change children's play. **Play should be directed by the children.** The teacher should occasionally join the play, but only for brief periods of time. Since children's experiences are varied and often limited, your role might be to demonstrate specific possibilities for play. For example, in the airline play described on page 50 you might say, "May I please have a baggage ticket for my suitcase?" or "Will you give me my boarding pass please?" These simple suggestions will guide children in their play and extend their knowledge of a real world situation.

- You can enhance these experiences by providing picture books appropriate for the center. In the examples above, books about traveling or flying would be appropriate.

- Invite visitors to the class to enrich the experiences of your students.

- Plan a field trip that correlates with the dramatic play center. For example, after using a post office center, children could write letters or cards and mail them at the local post office.

A Visit to the Doctor

This center can be a hospital, a dentist's office, or a veterinarian's office.

Play Props
Stethoscope
Cotton balls
Band-Aids
Bandages
Hot water bottle
Ice pack
White smocks
   (Dad's old shirts)
Nurse's cap
Flashlight
Blood pressure kit (toy)
Scale
Chairs
Cot
Skeleton
Crutches
Play thermometer
Dolls or stuffed animals
Tongue depressors

Plus Print
RX pad
Magazines
Eye chart
Appointment book
Medical books
Medical brochures
Pencils/pens
Clipboard and paper
Pictures/posters
Play money
Checks
Insurance forms
Height/weight chart
Business cards
Diplomas
Patient files
Magazines
Signs: Exit
        Dr. _____ 's Office
        Hours: _____
        Sign in here

Getting Started

- Introduce the various play props and talk about their uses.

- Dolls or stuffed animals can be the patients.

- Talk about things that happen in a doctor's office.

- Children can give examinations, bandage wounds, weigh and measure patients, treat an illness, discuss good health practices.

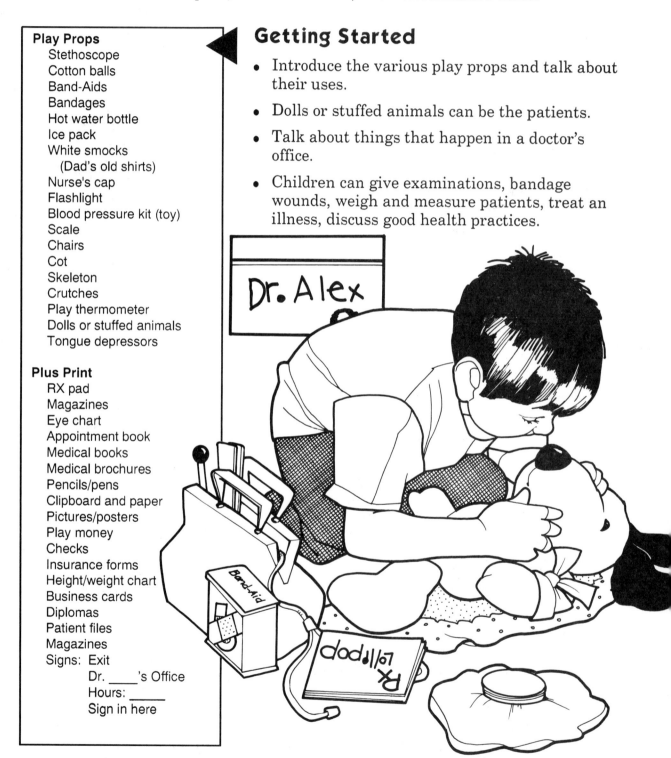

Adding Print

- To stimulate children to think about what goes on in a doctor's office, introduce the center with one of the books listed below.
- Add just a few print items at first. Start with a prescription pad, an appointment book, and patient files, since these are found in all doctors' offices. Allow children to explore their uses, giving guidance if needed.

▶ Suggested Books for the Doctor's Office

- *The Checkup* by Helen Oxenbury (Dial)
- *Corduroy Goes to the Doctor* by Don Freeman (Viking Press)
- *Going to the Doctor* by Fred Rogers (Putnam)
- *A Trip to the Doctor* by Margot Linn (Harper & Row)
- *When I See My Doctor* by Susan Kuklin (Bradbury Press)

My Favorite Restaurant

This center can also be set up as a fast food restaurant.

Play Props
  Table
  Chairs
  Dishes, cups
  Flatware
  Napkins
  Tablecloth
  Cooking utensils
  Kitchen appliances/equipment
    (sink, stove, oven)
  Chef's hat
  Apron
  Food (real or pretend)
  Bow ties for waiters
  Centerpiece for table
  Trays
  Cash register

Plus Print
  Order pad
  Pencils/pens
  Menu
  Advertising
  Play money
  Sales check
  Credit cards
  Recipes for the chef
  Paper place mats for children
    (pencil games)
  Name tags for waiters
  Signs: Menu board
         Daily specials
         Wait to Be Seated
         Name of restaurant

Getting Started

- Talk to the children about restaurants they have visited. Which is their favorite? What did the waiters/waitresses do? What did they eat? How was the food served? How was it paid for? What are the differences between a fast food restaurant and a more formal restaurant?

- Introduce the props and talk about possible uses for each. Help children decide how the restaurant should be set up. Where will the customers sit? Where will they wait to be seated? Where will they pay? Where is the kitchen?

- Discuss the various roles in a restaurant: customers, chefs, waiters, hostess, bus boy. Talk about what each one does. For instance, the waiter point outs the daily special, discusses dishes on the menu, takes the order, serves the food, adds up the bill, and clears the table.

- Nutrition and table manners can also be discussed.

I Can Read! I Can Write! Creative Teaching Press

Adding Print

- To start children thinking about their own restaurant experiences, introduce the center with one of the books listed below.

- Introduce the print items and allow children to discuss and explore their possible uses.

- Let children make signs and design menus. They can also decide where the signs are to be displayed.

▶ Suggested Books for the Restaurant

- *Curious George Goes to a Restaurant* by Margaret Rey and Alan Shalleck (Houghton Mifflin)
- *Eating Out* by Helen Oxenbury (Dial Books)
- *How My Parents Learned to Eat* by Ina R. Friedman (Houghton Mifflin)
- *Little Nino's Pizzeria* by Karen Barbour (Harcourt Brace Jovanovich)
- *Marge's Diner* by Gail Gibbons (T. Y. Crowell)

At the Airport

This center can also be a bus or a train station.

Play Props
Chairs
Ticket counter
Telephone for reservations
Luggage
Plane seats (numbered)
Instrument panel (box with knobs and dials)
Controls
Headsets
Microphone
Serving cart
Trays
Food
Cups, plates, flatware, napkins
Small pillows

Plus Print
Paper
Pencils/pens
Clipboard and paper
Tickets
Boarding passes
Baggage tags
Information brochures
Reservation list
In-flight magazines
Order pad
Emergency instruction card
Maps/flight charts
Signs: Arrival/Departure
         Exit
         Name of airline
         Check Baggage Here
         Gate __

Getting Started

- Discuss the children's prior experiences at an airport. Talk about the different roles: passengers, ticket agents, flight attendants, ground crew, and pilots.

- Let students help design the center. It could include one or all of the following: ticket counter, waiting area at the gate, plane, control tower, baggage claim area.

- Introduce the play props and discuss their possible uses.

- Children in various roles can pack luggage, purchase tickets, board the plane, eat/read on the plane, sell tickets, assign seats, take food orders, give safety instructions, load baggage onto the plane, direct takeoff, unload luggage, talk to passengers about the flight, and pilot the plane.

I Can Read! I Can Write! Creative Teaching Press

Adding Print

- Introduce the center with one of the books listed below.

- Add just a few print items at first, depending on the
roles children want to play. Begin with paper for a
reservations list, a couple of signs, baggage tags, and
tickets. Most children are familiar with these items.
Add other items as children are ready to expand their
play.

▶ Suggested Books for the Airport Center

- *Airport* by Byron Barton (T. Y. Crowell)
- *First Look at the Airport* by Dauphne Butler
(G. Stevens Children's Books)
- *Fly Away Home* by Eve Bunting
(Clarion Books)
- *Inside the Airport* by Mark Davies
(Contemporary Books)
- *Harry at the Airport* by Derek Radford
(Aladdin Books)

Mommy's or Daddy's Office

Play Props
Desk
Chair
Calculator
Family pictures for desk
Stapler
Paper clips
Scotch tape
Tape recorder
Telephone

Plus Print
Pencils/pens
Legal pads/paper
Forms/applications
Reference books
Telephone books
File folders
Computer
Typewriter
Maps or charts
Business cards
Magazines
Brochures/advertising items
Stamps and stamp pads
Calendar
Appointment book
Signs: Company name and logo
      Name plate on desk
      Department names

Getting Started

- Talk with children about experiences they have had in offices. Talk about the people one might see in an office, their different roles, and the different kinds of offices.

- Visit the school office to observe the activities.

- Introduce the play props and discuss their possible uses. Let children decide what type of office to set up and the purpose of the office. For example, if they set up a sales office, what product will the company sell?

- Depending on the kind of office, children can take orders; fill out forms; use the computer, typewriter, or calculator; make telephone calls; and write letters.

     I Can Read! I Can Write!   Creative Teaching Press

Adding Print

- Introduce the center with one of the books listed below.
- Add just a few print items at first such as paper and pencil, calendar, appointment book, and typewriter. Talk with the children about their uses. Watch for opportunities to expand children's knowledge by adding items. Talk about the importance of these items to most businesses.
- Allow children to make signs, name tags, and business cards.

Suggested Books for the Office Center

- *Daddies at Work* by Eve Merriam (Simon & Schuster)
- *I Can Be a Secretary* by Dee Lillegard (Childrens Press)
- *If I Could Work* by Terence Black (Lippincott)
- *Mommies at Work* by Eve Merriam (Simon & Schuster)
- *Mommy's Office* by Barbara Hazen (Atheneum)
- *My Mommy Makes Money* by Joyce Mitchell (Little, Brown and Company)

At the Clothing Store

Play Props
- Cash register
- Clothing items to sell
- Accessories
  (jewelry, ties, belts, hats)
- Mannequin
- Display areas for sale
  items
- Sales counter
- Shopping bags
- Hangers
- Mirrors
- Fitting Room

Plus Print
- Pens/pencils
- Sales receipts
- Price tags
- Labels for items
- Play money
- Credit cards
- Checks
- Advertising
- Name tags for employees
- Signs: To advertise a sale
  - Name of store
  - Fitting Room

Getting Started

- Talk with children about their experiences at a clothing store. What kinds of clothes were in the store? What did the store employees do?

- Introduce the play props to the children and discuss their uses.

- Children can set up displays, try on clothes, make purchases, ring up sales, hang up clothes, and assist customers.

I Can Read! I Can Write!

Adding Print

- Introduce the center with one of the books listed below.
- Add just a few print items at first. Talk about the uses of different kinds of signs and how items are priced and labeled.
- Model how to write up a sales check.
- Have students make signs for sale items.

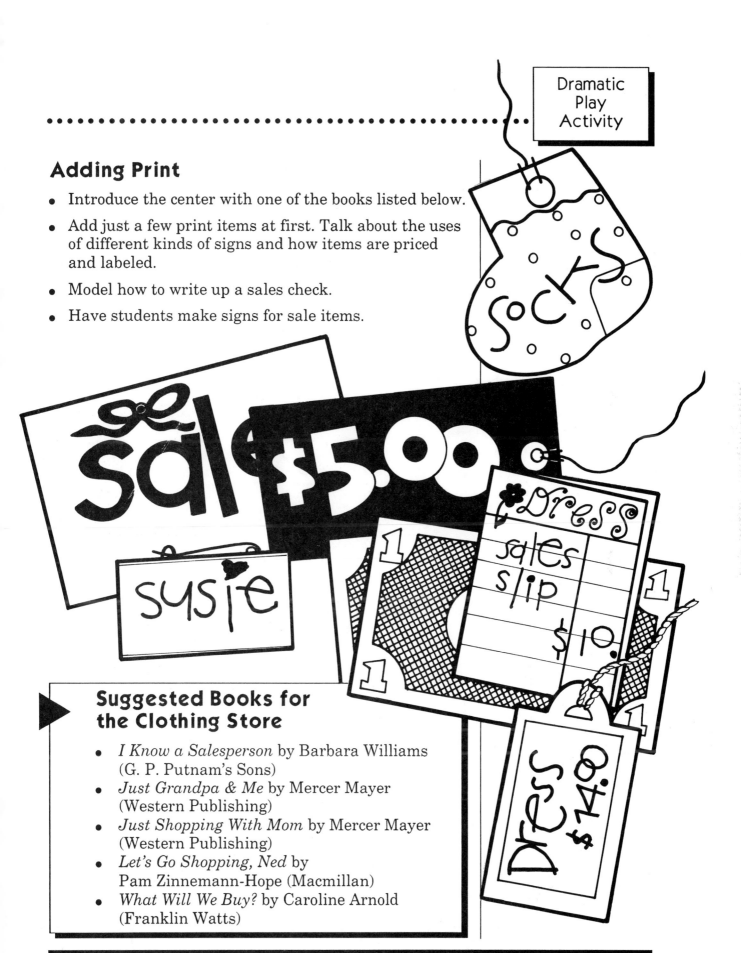

Suggested Books for the Clothing Store

- *I Know a Salesperson* by Barbara Williams (G. P. Putnam's Sons)
- *Just Grandpa & Me* by Mercer Mayer (Western Publishing)
- *Just Shopping With Mom* by Mercer Mayer (Western Publishing)
- *Let's Go Shopping, Ned* by Pam Zinnemann-Hope (Macmillan)
- *What Will We Buy?* by Caroline Arnold (Franklin Watts)

Let's Put on a Play

Play Props
Ticket booth
Cash register
Stage
Costumes or puppets
Chairs
Flashlight for usher
Refreshment counter
Intermission snacks

Plus Print
Tickets
Program
Play money
Credit card/slips
Posters
Scripts or books
 students can perform
Signs: Exit
 Ticket price list

Getting Started

- Talk with children about their experiences going to the theater (play, puppet show, movie).

- Talk about the roles of the ticket seller, ushers, performers, and audience. Children can collect tickets, sell refreshments, seat members of the audience, or perform in the play.

- Introduce the various play props and talk about their uses.

Adding Print

- Introduce the center with one of the books listed below.
- Discuss how children can adapt familiar stories for informal performances.
- Model how to make programs and posters for the performance.

▶ Suggested Books for the Theater

- *Angelina on Stage* by Katharine Holabird (Crown)
- *Pet of the Met* by Lydia Freeman (Viking)
- *Starring First Grade* by Miriam Cohen (Greenwillow)
- *Theater Magic: Behind the Scenes at a Children's Theater* by Cheryl Walsh Bellville (Carolrhoda)

Additional Suggestions for Adding Print to Dramatic Play Centers

Police or Fire Station

Children can keep records, dispatch officers, write tickets or reports, design "wanted" posters, take fingerprints, go to court, and be lawyers.

Gas Station

Children can pump gas, write tickets, handle money, read repair instructions and labels, and identify different kinds of cars.

Pet Store

Children can care for animals, make signs, handle money, read labels on pet products, and talk to customers about pet care.

Post Office

Children can write, address, and mail letters; wrap and weigh packages; decide on postage; stamp packages and other mail; sell stamps; handle money; and deliver mail to the addressee.

Grocery Store

Children can take inventory, make signs, read labels, stock shelves, price items, buy groceries, and check groceries.

I Can Read! I Can Write!   Creative Teaching Press

Hair Salon or Barber Shop

Children can pretend to wash, cut, and style hair; look at magazines while waiting; make appointments; keep client records; take money and make change. Customers can be students, dolls, or stuffed animals.

Weather Station

Children can make weather charts showing temperature and weather conditions, post the weather on a map, use a thermometer, and do a weather show for TV.

Flower Shop

Children can arrange flowers, price flower arrangements, take orders, receive payments, purchase flowers, and make signs.

Art Gallery

Children can create and display their own artwork, labeled with the name of the artist and the title of the piece. Information can be written about the artist. The gallery owner can sell artwork to customers.

▶ Print can be added to almost any dramatic play situation. Just let your imagination go!

Dear Parents,

On Thursday, September 28, we are sponsoring our first Family Literacy Night. We would like you and your child to join us for a fun evening of reading and writing activities.

Sincerely,

The Kindergarten Teachers

5 Getting Parents Involved

 ## Why do parents need to be involved?

A parent is a child's first and most important teacher. Before a child ever comes to school, he is already developing as a reader and writer. This is especially true if the child is being raised in a truly literate environment where parents understand the importance of reading and the uses of print.

It is up to you to keep parents involved in their children's academic growth and development. Children are much more likely to take an interest in reading and writing if they receive the same message both at home and at school. By working together, you can help children realize that reading and writing are important and fun.

On pages 68–74 you will find a selection of letters that will help strengthen the home-school connection. You may use each letter as is or as a guideline for writing your own personal letters to parents. The letters are informative and offer suggestions on involving parents in literacy development. The topics include:

- **Parents as Literacy Teachers** (literacy development in the home)

- **Environmental Print** (encouraging awareness of and collecting samples for school)

- **Writing Box** (a gift that encourages writing)

- **Family Literacy Night** (a fun, idea-packed evening of reading-writing activities)

- **High Adventure Backpacks** (school-home activities designed around a theme)

- **Book Friends** (a school-home book loan program)

- **Read Me a Story** (effective read-aloud techniques)

Family Literacy Night

Thursday 7:00-8:30p.m.

Dear Parent(s),

Although you may not have considered it, you are your child's first and most important teacher. Children begin to develop as readers and writers before they ever come to school. You help your child learn to use print in all of its forms whenever you do the following:

- make a grocery list
- read a newspaper
- read the mail
- look at a magazine
- look up a number in a phone book
- write a letter
- write a check
- make a "to do" list
- read a menu in a restaurant

These activities make your child aware that the little squiggly things we call letters are one way to communicate. Take a few minutes to think about the many ways you use print every day. Now think about all those everyday tasks your child could help you do:

- read traffic signs and store signs
- write letters to grandparents
- follow a simple recipe
- make lists for chores, errands, groceries
- look at the newspaper
- take a trip to the library or the bookstore
- read labels on food boxes
- write down a phone message

These are all literacy events—events in our daily lives which can help develop children's reading and writing skills. By participating in these activities, children gain an understanding of the many uses of print. Please keep me informed of literacy events in your home as we work together to help our new readers and writers continue to grow.

Sincerely,

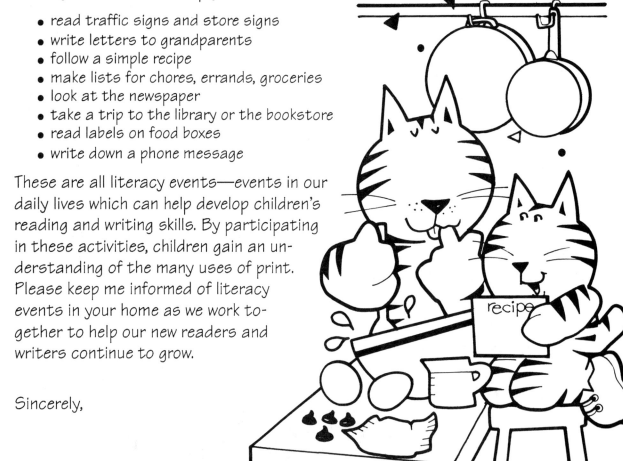

Dear Parent(s),

Environmental print is a term that the parents of every young reader should know. It is the print we see all around us: the labels on the cereal and peanut butter your child loves, the logo on a favorite fast food restaurant, and the stop sign at the corner. It is print we recognize from the colors, pictures, and shapes that surround it.

Environmental print is usually the first print children recognize. Then they move on to reading the words, first without the color and then without the pictures and shapes that surround them. Recognizing environmental print makes children feel successful at "reading" and motivates them to read more.

You can encourage your child to read environmental print. All day long there are opportunities to point out print to your child. As you prepare meals, read the labels of food items. When you run errands, read traffic signs and billboards. When you walk into a place of business, read signs and the labels of the products being sold.

Help me bring environmental print to the classroom. Please begin collecting familiar print samples with your child. Newspaper and magazine ads are an excellent source for print samples, as well as coupons and labels on packaged foods. Send in as many samples as you can; repeats are welcome. These samples will be used for various activities, including puzzles, educational games, and a class scrapbook.

Please start collecting today! Your child will be proud to show classmates how well he/she can read. As always, thank you for helping our young readers to grow.

Sincerely,

Betty Crocker® and Super Moist® are registered trademarks of General Mills, Inc., used with permission.

The Perfect Gift—A Writing Box

Dear Parent(s),

Looking for the perfect gift for your child? Ready to get away from expensive breakable plastic toys? Need something different for your child to take to a birthday party? How about a Writing Box? What better way to encourage a child to read and write!

A Writing Box is a container filled with a variety of writing supplies guaranteed to capture the interest of a child. Choose a container that is big enough to hold a lot of goodies but small enough for a child to carry (lunch pail, cleaning caddy, picnic basket, plastic shoe box, food tin). It's also fun to have the container personalized with the child's name.

The contents of the Writing Box might include:

- Paper (various sizes, colors, textures and shapes, usually unlined)
- Note pads
- Pencils (colored and lead)
- Markers
- Crayons
- Chalk
- Mini-chalkboard
- Magnetic alphabet letters and numbers
- Metal surface such as a cookiesheet for magnetic letters

- Old magazines
- Pencil game books
- Stickers
- Blank books
- Calendar
- Rubber stamps and stamp pad
- Stencils (shapes, letters, numbers)
- Envelopes
- "Stamps"
- Small books
- Watercolor paints
- Playdough

Have fun putting the box together, and please let me know if you have any suggestions for additions to the above list.

Sincerely,

You're Invited to a Family Literacy Night

Dear Parent(s),

On _____, the _____ grade teachers will be sponsoring our first Family Literacy Night. We would like you and your child to join us for a fun evening of reading and writing activities. We will introduce you to a number of new and exciting children's books and ways to share these books with your child.

You will learn about parent resources for encouraging reading and writing at home and the importance of these activities to your child's success as a lifelong reader. You will also learn how to choose the right books for your child and techniques for reading aloud.

This will be an informal family evening built around activities you and your child can share. There will be refreshments and a book giveaway, as well as other treats and surprises.

Please plan to attend this very special family evening and help to ensure your child's future success!

Sincerely,

High Adventure Backpacks

Dear Parent(s),

Next week your child will be introduced to a new home-school activity called "High Adventure Backpacks." Each backpack will contain one or two books and a number of reading and writing activities based on a selected theme. Every week, several children will have the opportunity to check out a backpack to take home.

Each backpack will also contain a checklist of the included activities and a blank book to be used as a journal. Please encourage your child to do as many activities as possible. Some activities require parent participation.

Before returning the backpack, please have your child write a response to the activities in the journal and write your own response as well. (For example, how your child enjoyed the activity, ways to improve an activity, a favorite book that fits the theme.) This will help me identify the activities that are of value to you and your child.

The backpacks will be coming home on a Monday and **must be returned by Friday**. This will give me time to restock them for the following week.

I look forward to sharing this activity with you and your child. As always, if you should have any questions or suggestions, please feel free to contact me.

Sincerely,

Book Friends

Dear Parent(s),

Just as your child brings friends home to meet you, he/she will be bringing home "book friends" too. On a daily basis beginning next Monday, students will have the opportunity to take home a "book friend" of their choice. Each book will be stored in a gallon-size resealable plastic bag. The following check-out system will be used:

1. One book may be checked out at a time.

2. A new book may be checked out as soon as the first book is returned.

3. All books must be returned by Friday.

When a "book friend" comes home, take a few minutes to share the book with your child. Read together and discuss the story. Encourage your child to read to you, and try some of the extension activities we did at Family Literacy Night. When you are too busy to read, re-member that favorite stuffed animals make great reading buddies for young children.

As part of the Book Friends Program, each child will be asked to share at least one "book friend" a week with classmates. A record will be kept of the books your child takes home. You are welcome to look at this record at any time, review the books that have been read, and assess your child's participation in the Book Friends Program.

Thank you for helping to ensure the success of this reading program.

Sincerely,

Read Me a Story

Dear Parent(s),

Most educators now realize that the single most important thing parents can do to ensure their child's success as a reader is to read to him every day. Included below is a list of tips on how to make story time pleasurable for both of you:

1. Pick a time when you can devote your full attention to your child. It may be before dinner, during bath time, or at bedtime; these uninterrupted few minutes are important.

2. Take time to talk about the cover of the book before you start to read. Point out the author and the illustrator and discuss what those terms mean. Ask your child to predict what the story is about on the basis of the cover illustration and refer back to those predictions as you read.

3. Read at a comfortable pace for you and your child.

4. Help your child connect print to speech by pointing to the words in the text as you read.

5. Encourage your child to ask questions about the story and take time to ask questions as you read.

6. When you finish reading, talk about the story. Then ask your child to tell the story in his or her own words.

7. Read your child's favorite books over and over. Studies show that each time a child listens to the same story, new kinds of learning take place. When your child knows the book by heart, let him "read" it to you!

You will soon discover that there is no greater joy than helping your child learn to read. Bring that joy into your home today.

Sincerely,

Resources

 ## Do I Have a Print-Rich Environment? (A Checklist)

Creating the Environment

❑ Are there books and writing materials in a reading/writing center and in various places throughout the room?

❑ Are children given opportunities to read and write throughout the day?

❑ Are there places for children to display messages or information they wish to share?

❑ Is there print of some kind at each learning center?

❑ Are there various print information sources, such as maps, charts, globes, pictures, and books?

❑ Is there a wide variety of writing tools and materials?

❑ Is there a wide variety of other items which will encourage reading and writing: flannel boards, puppets, tape recorder, letter games.

❑ Are there a lot of things to talk, read, and write about?

❑ Are print displays kept current?

❑ Are there comfortable, accessible places which invite and encourage students to read and write?

❑ Are there books of all kinds displayed in such a way that students are encouraged to use them?

❑ Are songs, poetry, and students' stories displayed?

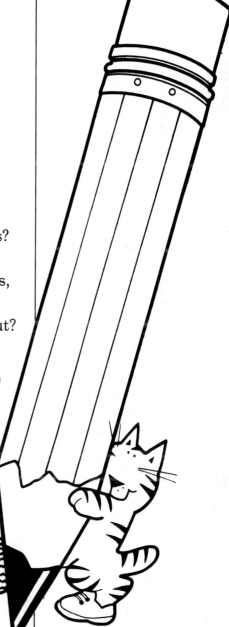

Using Environmental Print

❏ Is there evidence of environmental print in classroom centers and displays?

❏ Are children given opportunities to interact with environmental print samples?

Using Functional Print

❏ Are labels and print materials combined with pictures, objects, and other nonprint items?

❏ Are printed directions used by the teacher instead of oral directions to help manage the classroom?

❏ Is print a part of most daily classroom routines?

❏ Is print included in classroom displays?

Adding Print to Dramatic Play

❏ Are children given opportunities to explore the many uses of print through dramatic play?

❏ Do materials provided in dramatic play settings encourage the use of print?

Involving Parents

❏ Have you explained to parents how children develop reading and writing skills?

❏ Do you provide opportunities for parents to become involved in their children's literacy development both at home and at school?

For Further Reading

Jett-Simpson, Mary. *Adventuring With Books.* 9th ed. Illinois: National Council of Teachers of English, 1989.

Kobrin, Beverly. *Eyeopeners.* New York: Viking, 1988.

Lima, Carolyn. *A to Zoo: Subject Access to Children's Picture Books.* New York: Bowker, 1982.

Loughlin, Catherine E. and Mavis D. Martin. *Supporting Literacy: Developing Effective Learning Environments.* New York: Teacher's College Press, 1987.

Morrow, Lesley M. *Literacy Development in the Early Years.* New Jersey: Prentice-Hall, 1989.

Sampson, Michael R. *The Pursuit of Literacy.* Iowa: Kendall-Hunt Publishing Co., 1986.

Strickland, Dorothy S. and Lesley M. Morrow, eds. *Emerging Literacy: Young Children Learn to Read and Write.* Delaware: International Reading Association, 1989.

Classroom Cookbooks

Bruno, Janet. *Book Cooks.* Creative Teaching Press, 1991.

Catron, Carol E. *Cooking Up a Story.* T. S. Dennison, 1986.

Faggella, Cathy. *Concept Cookery.* First Teacher's Press, 1985.

Jenkins, Karen S. *Kinder-Krunchies.* Discovery Toys, 1982.

Veitch, Beverly and Thelma Harms. *Cook and Learn: Pictorial Single Portion Recipes.* Addison-Wesley Publishing Company, 1981.

NOTES

Grades 3–6

20 Thinking Questions for
PATTERN BLOCKS

Kathryn Walker   Cynthia Reak   Kelly Stewart

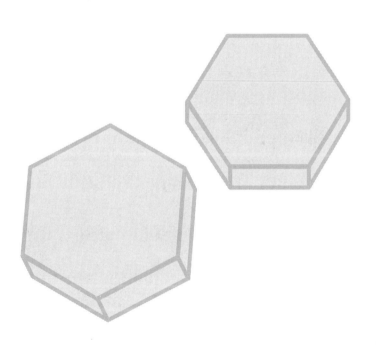

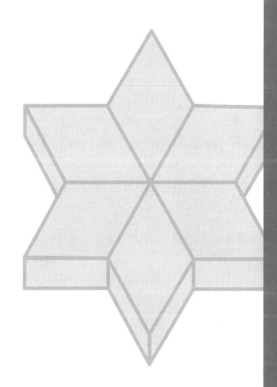

Creative Publications®

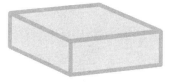

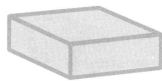

Acknowledgments

Editor: Sharon Wheeler

Production Editor: Ann Roper

Classroom Coordinators: Kay Hatfield and Cindy Maynes Lopez

Creative Director: Ken Shue

Designer: Janice Kawamoto

Production Coordinator: Joe Shines

Production: Carlisle Communications, LTD

Illustrator: DJ Simison

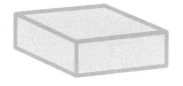

Thanks to the teachers and the students of the many classrooms who tried out these activities. Their original work can be seen on pages viii–xi of this book.

©1995 Creative Publications
Two Prudential Plaza
Chicago, IL 60601
Printed in the United States of America

ISBN: 1-56107-795-X
6 7 8 9 10. 04 03 02 01 00

Contents

THE CHANGING ROLES OF TEACHERS AND STUDENTS

In years past, the role of the mathematics teacher was to present students with rules and procedures, then give them problems to practice. The role of the student was to practice diligently in order to remember the information or procedures presented. Most time was spent on computation.

In today's world, mathematics is much broader than computation. Emphasis is on communication and complex problem solving. Rather than teaching specific rules for specific problems, teachers must help students develop thinking tools so that they are ready to meet the challenge of any new problem with confidence and enthusiasm.

It must be remembered that the purpose of education is not to fill the minds of students with facts…it is to teach them to think, if that is possible, and always to think for themselves.

—Robert Hutchins

What is the philosophy?

20 Thinking Questions is a series of 15 resource books created for teachers who wish to include investigative problem solving in their mathematics curriculum. Each of the **20 Thinking Questions** books focuses on students' use of manipulatives to solve problems having mutiple solutions or solution methods. As part of the solution process, students write about their thinking prior to engaging in classroom discussions. Working with manipulatives gives students an opportunity to explore abstract concepts while manipulating concrete objects. Writing about one's thinking challenges students to clarify their ideas and provides teachers with insights into each student's thinking and level of understanding.

Your role as teacher is to pose a problem and then to encourage students to follow their own logical path in finding solutions that make sense to them. Greater emphasis is placed on the students' reaching an understanding rather than on them finding a correct answer.

How is this book organized?

Each book contains 20 questions emphasizing problem solving using a specific manipulative. In general, questions in each book are arranged from easiest to most difficult. However, depending on your students' backgrounds and prior experiences, you may find a different ordering of questions more appropriate for your class. Feel free to select those questions that best fit your students' abilities and interests.

When should I use these questions?

You can use **20 Thinking Questions** in a variety of ways, but we suggest that you use the questions in this book to create a "thinking strand" within your current curriculum. Most questions will take one, perhaps two, class periods to complete. Try one question every other week or choose another book in the series to provide enough questions for each week of the school year.

How is each question organized?

The format of each question in this book is clear and easy to follow. The four-page question layout gives you all the information you need to help facilitate student learning.

The **QUESTION STATEMENT** lets you know what is being asked of students. Review these statements to help you decide if the question is appropriate for the developmental level of your students. You may find that you need to review concepts prior to introducing a question.

MATERIALS tells you at a glance what you need to prepare for the day's lesson.

INTRODUCING THE QUESTION walks you through an appropriate whole-class activity or discussion. It provides you with the necessary definitions to review prior to starting the question or gives you a simpler question to do as a class together.

Students will approach problems in many different ways. Some students may have difficulty understanding how to start while other students may finish very quickly. **WHAT SHOULD YOU DO IF...** offers you tips on what you should do if your students perform in a certain way.

What can you expect from your students? There isn't one right answer or solution method. **WHAT YOU MIGHT SEE** will give you some sample answers or solution methods. Don't expect your students to come up with some or all of these examples. Each student is different, and the thinking that emerges will range widely. The point is for you to become aware of the diversity in your classroom.

Has the student accomplished the expected outcomes? **WHAT TO LOOK FOR IN STUDENT'S WORK** tells you what to look for, helping you assess each student's work.

To enhance the learning potential of each question, give students time to discuss and to share the variety of solution methods they found. This is the time to post students' recordings or to let the class walk around and view each other's work. **QUESTIONS FOR DISCUSSION** lists several open-ended questions that you can use to stimulate class discussion. If your class takes an interesting detour, go with it! The key is to let students explain their thinking.

Students will learn a lot from the class discussion, exchanging ideas and reformulating their own thinking. The **JOURNAL REFLECTION** gives students a chance to write about this thinking. It reflects new information and understanding students may glean from actively talking with their classmates. This writing is an extension of the writing students do in the process of answering the question, where they clarify their thinking of their solution. The Journal Reflection takes it a step further, allowing students to reflect on and to assess what they have learned. Choose the one Journal Reflection question that best fits your needs.

How should I organize my class?

During the course of each question's exploration, the class will be organized in different ways. You will meet with the group as a whole to introduce the question and for the follow-up discussion after students have worked on their solutions. Students will work with a partner or in a group to explore and to answer each question. As a culmination to the day's investigation, students will work individually to answer a journal reflection question.

How should I organize the manipulatives?

The complete manipulative kit for **20 Thinking Questions for Pattern Blocks** is designed to provide a sufficient number of blocks for 16 pairs of students. The materials list will alert you as to when students will require a particular number or type of block. When no specific blocks are called for, students will need a "set" of Pattern Blocks containing: 9 each of green triangles, blue rhombuses, tan rhombuses, and red trapezoids; and 4 each of yellow hexagons and orange squares. Students can help you prepare these materials ahead of time. In addition you will want to have several copies of the 1-centimeter and triangle grid papers available for each student's recordings.

If your students are using a manipulative for the first time, allow them a period of free exploration to become familiar with the materials so they will be ready to focus on a question's solution rather than on the workings of the manipulative.

What about assessment?

If you choose to assess your students' work, there are a variety of approaches you can use. Having students keep a portfolio of their work will allow you and your students to identify growth in thinking, in problem solving, and in writing about their thinking. Observing and talking with students while they work will give you insights into their level of understanding, their confidence in approaching open-ended problems, and their ability to interact with others.

If you prefer to do a more formal assessment of students' work, the "What to Look for in Student's Work" questions will serve as a guide to help you evaluate each student's response. The Journal Reflection questions will give you insights into your students' attitudes about math.

The range of student abilities and responses will vary widely on these questions depending on each student's level of development.

A Thinking Question in Action

Mrs. Chase presents this question to her fifth grade class:

CAN YOU MAKE A DESIGN WHERE $\frac{1}{4}$ OF THE AREA IS GREEN?

Can you make a design or pattern where $\frac{1}{4}$ of the area is green? Use your Pattern Blocks to make a design. Then record your design and explain how you know that $\frac{1}{4}$ of the area is green.

Each pair of students receives a set of Pattern Blocks (9 red, 9 blue, 9 green, and 4 yellow) and paper, pencils, and crayons for recording. To introduce the question, Mrs. Chase shows a green block on the overhead projector and tells the class that the green triangle has an area of 1. She shows several other blocks individually and asks the class to tell the area of each.

The class seems to catch on quickly, so Mrs. Chase shows them a design made with several blocks. **What is the area of this design? How do you know?** Several students volunteer to tell the area and explain their thinking. Mrs. Chase encourages the class to decide together if these explanations are correct. **What do the rest of you think? Does anyone disagree? Can anyone explain his or her thinking in a different way?**

Mrs. Chase explains to the class that their challenge for today is to create designs where $\frac{1}{4}$ of the area is green. **Make a recording of your design and explain how you know $\frac{1}{4}$ of the area is green.** Pairs are quickly "heads down" over their Pattern Blocks as they begin to create designs.

As Students Begin to Work

Mrs. Chase walks around the room, watching and listening. Some students make designs but do not follow the rule of "$\frac{1}{4}$ of the area is green." Mrs. Chase knows that the students have had many free-exploration opportunities with the Pattern Blocks and should be able to approach this challenge. She asks questions to focus their thinking on the area aspect of the task. **What is the total area of your design? What is the area of the green blocks?**

One pair creates the same design as the pair next to them and Mrs. Chase knows that for these students, this is a good way to begin. It is more important that the students are able to explain how the area is $\frac{1}{4}$ green than to create an original design at first. She decides to check back in a few minutes and encourage this pair. **Can you make a design that no one else has discovered?**

Nancy has had difficulty in the past putting her thinking into words, so Mrs. Chase was pleased to see three different examples on her report. The last example in Nancy's work shows a real attempt to use mathematical logic: "Blue equals 2 greens, so that's 2, 2, 2, 2." This is a real step forward for Nancy.

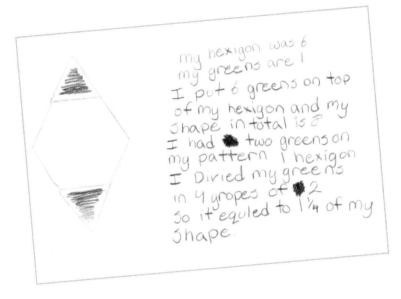

my hexigon was 6
my greens are 1
I put 6 greens on top
of my hexigon and my
shape in total is 8
I had two greens on
my pattern 1 hexigon
I Divied my greens
in 4 gropes of 2
so it equled to 1¼ of my
shape.

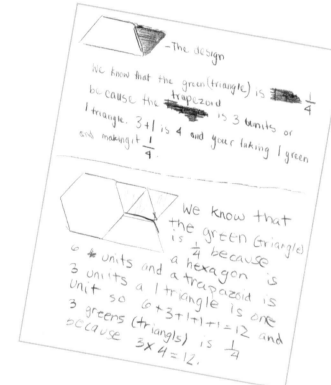

-The design

We know that the green (triangle) is ¼
be cause the trapezoid is 3 units or
1 triangle. 3+1 is 4 and your taking 1 green
and makingit ¼.

We know that
the green (triangle)
is ¼ because
a hexagon is
6 units and a trapazoid is
3 units a 1 triangle is one
Unit so 6+3+1+1+1=12 and
3 greens (triangls) is ¼
because 3×4=12.

Andrea and Todd work together to create and to discuss designs, then they each make their own recording. Their work shows a good ability to use logical thinking in writing to prove that their designs are correct. They explain to Mrs. Chase that they are able to write about their thinking "because we talk it out first."

ASKING EFFECTIVE QUESTIONS

Talking about ideas is an important aspect of creating confident mathematical thinkers. While students are working and during class discussions, it is important that your questioning style encourages students to think and to talk about their thinking.

■ ASK OPEN-ENDED QUESTIONS.

Avoid questions with simple answers, especially *yes* or *no*.

■ ALLOW TIME FOR EVERYONE TO THINK.

Ask a question and say, *Talk to your partner for a few minutes and be ready with an idea.* This encourages everyone to think about the question instead of relying on the "quick" students to do all the talking.

■ ENCOURAGE STUDENTS TO TALK TO EACH OTHER.

A discussion is a back and forth conversation. Get your students talking to each other, not responding to you.

■ TAKE ON THE ROLE OF THE FRIENDLY SKEPTIC.

Respond equally to right and wrong answers, saying, *Well, I'm not sure...what do the rest of you think?* Let the rightness or wrongness of answers come from the class, not from you.

■ CHALLENGE STUDENTS TO ASK THEIR OWN QUESTIONS.

Pushing beyond the original question to new questions and answers is an important move toward higher-order thinking. Ask, *What is another question you could ask about this?* Take time to explore some of these student generated questions.

■ GIVE GOOD THINKING TIME TO DEVELOP.

Include thinking questions and good class discussions in your curriculum throughout the year. You will see an amazing change in your students as their confidence soars!

Questions for Discussion

After the students finish their reports, it is time for a class discussion. Mrs. Chase knows that presenting designs will be difficult, as it will be hard for everyone to see the traced designs and even more difficult for the students to sketch them on the chalkboard. Even using transparent pieces on the overhead would be too time consuming.

Mrs. Chase delays the discussion and asks each pair to turn in one traced design. She uses a copier to make transparencies of these designs and lets students use them in their discussion the next day.

Mrs. Chase begins the discussion by asking several questions:

- **What does your design look like? Show it on the overhead projector.**
- **How do you know $\frac{1}{4}$ of the area is green?**
- **Did anyone find another design where the area is $\frac{1}{4}$ green?**

Students are eager to use their design transparencies, and several pairs who are often quiet in discussions volunteer to share their thinking.

Journal Reflection

Following the class discussion, Mrs. Chase asks the students to write in their math journals. The question she chooses is:

> What Pattern Blocks did you use most frequently? Why do you think so?

Maria's journal report explains that green is used most often. She goes on to give a "for instance" to prove her thinking.

I used the green most frequently. I think I did because (for instance) you could do 10 ~~diffrent~~ designs and have 2 or 3 greens in each design. Plus we also had to have atleast 1/4 of the design be green.

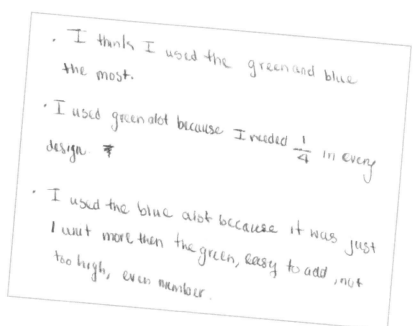

. I thinks I used the green and blue the most.

. I used green alot because I needed $\frac{1}{4}$ in every design.

. I used the blue alot because it was just I want more then the green, easy to add, not too high, even number.

Marshall's journal entry goes a little further. He includes blue with green as most frequently used and gives several reasons why blue works well. It is important to ask students to analyze why they think things turn out the way they do. This encourages important reflective thinking.

WRITING ABOUT MATHEMATICAL THINKING

Just as talking about thinking is important so is writing about thinking. The ability to explain ideas and findings to others is a critical tool for a future in which good communication continues to be a valued skill.

■ HAVE STUDENTS RECORD ON BLANK PAPER.

Organizing ideas and putting them on paper is an important part of solving any problem. Prepared worksheets do half of the work for students.

■ OBSERVE THE UNIQUENESS OF EACH STUDENT'S WORK.

When students are challenged to solve a problem in their own way and to report in their own way, each recording will be unique.

■ TAKE THE TIME TO COMMENT ON STUDENTS' WRITING.

Your comments will encourage students to improve their writing. Ask questions and give suggestions instead of making corrections.

■ USE PAIR AS WELL AS INDIVIDUAL REPORTS.

Working in pairs to solve and to discuss problems is often a good model. Reporting findings and ideas, however, should sometimes be done together, sometimes alone.

■ ASK STUDENTS TO REVISE THEIR WORK AT TIMES.

Let some writing be informal, a way of collecting ideas. Other times, have students revise their reports, making them ready to show to parents or to display in the hallway or in class booklets.

■ LET STUDENTS REPORT FROM OTHERS' RECORDINGS.

For another view of the importance of good communication, have students trade papers and report to the class about another pair's work using only their written report.

About the 20 Thinking Questions Series

20 Thinking Questions is a series of 15 books created to promote good mathematical thinking in primary through middle grade classrooms. Each book focuses on one manipulative and the many interesting questions that can be explored using that manipulative. Each book has a companion kit of manipulatives. If you and your students have enjoyed thinking about the questions in this book, try some of the other books! See a current Creative Publications catalog for prices.

Primary

20 Thinking Questions for Pattern Blocks, 31300
  Classroom Kit, 31365
20 Thinking Questions for LinkerCubes, 31301
  Classroom Kit, 31366
20 Thinking Questions for Base Ten Blocks, 31302
  Classroom Kit, 31367
20 Thinking Questions for Shapes and Sizes Attribute Pieces, 31303
  Classroom Kit, 31368
20 Thinking Questions for Sorting Treasures, 31304
  Classroom Kit, 31369

Intermediate

20 Thinking Questions for Pattern Blocks, 31305
  Classroom Kit, 31370
20 Thinking Questions for Rainbow Cubes, 31306
  Classroom Kit, 31371
20 Thinking Questions for Base Ten Blocks, 31307
  Classroom Kit, 31372
20 Thinking Questions for Fraction Circles, 31308
  Classroom Kit, 31373
20 Thinking Questions for Geoboards, 31309
  Classroom Kit, 31374

Middle School

20 Thinking Questions for Pattern Blocks, 31310
  Classroom Kit, 31375
20 Thinking Questions for Rainbow Cubes, 31311
  Classroom Kit, 31376
20 Thinking Questions for Base Ten Blocks, 31312
  Classroom Kit, 31377
20 Thinking Questions for Fraction Circles, 31313
  Classroom Kit, 31378
20 Thinking Questions for Geoboards, 31314
  Classroom Kit, 31379

20 Thinking Questions for
PATTERN BLOCKS

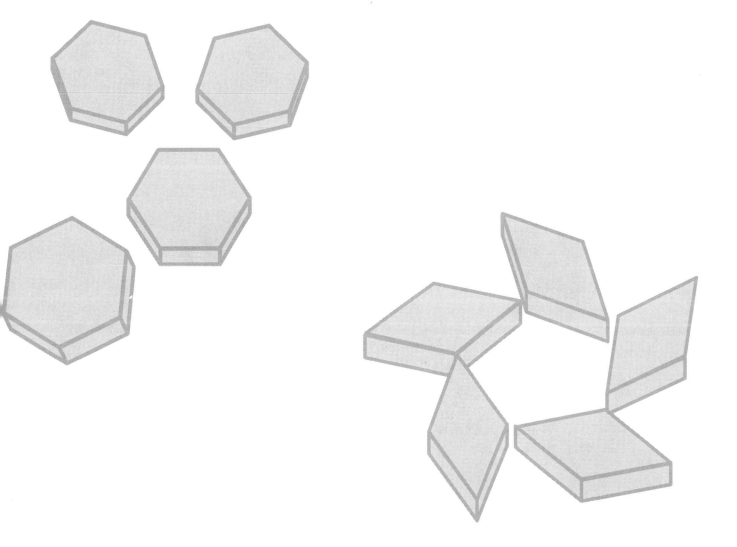

1 How many blocks will there be?

Use your Pattern Blocks to make this pattern: red, red, blue, green, red, red, blue, green. When there are 14 blue blocks, how many green and red blocks will there be? Make a recording of your work and explain how you figured the number of green and red blocks.

MATERIALS

For each pair of students
- Pattern Blocks (9 red, 9 green, and 9 blue)
- paper, pencils, and crayons for recording

For the overhead projector
- Pattern Blocks

INTRODUCING THE QUESTION

1 On the overhead projector, show this pattern and have students identify the pattern.

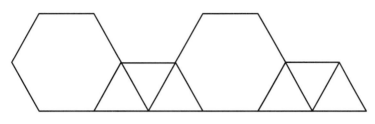

2 Suppose this pattern continued. **When there are 12 blocks, how many blocks will be yellow?** (3) **How many blocks will be green?** (9) **How do you know?** Allow students to share their explanations.

3 Show this pattern on the overhead projector: red, red, blue, green, red, red, blue, green. Have students work with their partners to solve today's question. **Make this pattern: red, red, blue, green, red, red, blue, green. When there are 14 blue blocks, how many green and red blocks will there be? Make a recording of your work and explain how you know the number of green and red blocks.**

WHAT SHOULD YOU DO IF . . .

▶ Some students find the number of green and red blocks total 14 blocks?

These students may not have heard or understood the question correctly. It's a good idea to post the question somewhere in the classroom for students to refer to while they are working.

▶ Some students think they can't solve the question without more Pattern Blocks?

Students will discover that they don't have enough blocks to solve the problem directly. Encourage students to invent alternative ways to find the answer: drawing pictures, tearing colored paper, making marks on paper, sharing blocks with another pair. Resist helping; let the students think of these ways themselves. **Can you think of another way to make the entire pattern?**

WHAT YOU MIGHT SEE

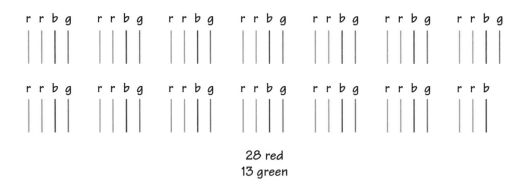

28 red
13 green

Some students may find a solution by drawing or by making marks to represent the blocks.

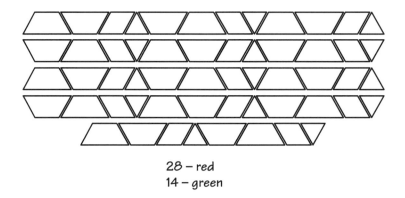

28 – red
14 – green

Some students may count the same number of green and blue blocks, not considering the blue block comes before the green block in the pattern.

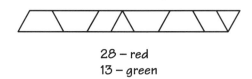

28 – red
13 – green

Some students may be able to find the number of green and red blocks without modeling the entire pattern.

WHAT TO LOOK FOR IN STUDENT'S WORK

Was the student able to state correctly the number of red and green blocks when there are 14 blue blocks?

Did the student clearly explain how he figured the number of red and green blocks?

QUESTIONS FOR DISCUSSION

- When there are 12 blue blocks, how many red blocks do you think there will be?

- How do you know?

- Does anyone think there will be a different number of red blocks?

- How many green blocks do you think there will be? How did you figure this number?

- Did anyone figure a different number of green blocks?

- When there are 12 red blocks, how many blue blocks do you think there will be?

JOURNAL REFLECTION

Describe a situation where patterns can help make predictions.

Is there more than one way to find a solution to today's question? Explain your thinking.

2 How many different shapes can you make?

Use 5 orange squares. Arrange the squares to make different shapes. How many different shapes can you make? Record each shape and explain how you know all the shapes are different.

MATERIALS

For each pair of students

- Pattern Blocks (5 orange)
- 1-Inch Grid Paper (p. 82)
- paper and pencils for recording

For the overhead projector

- Pattern Blocks (5 orange)

INTRODUCING THE QUESTION

1 Show 5 orange squares on the overhead projector. **How many different ways do you think you can arrange these blocks?**

2 Explain to students that whole sides of squares must touch. Use Pattern Block squares to show some examples and incorrect examples of arrangements on the overhead projector. **Before you begin, let's go over a few "rules."**

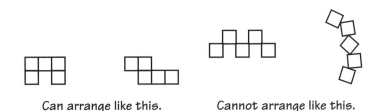

Can arrange like this.　　　Cannot arrange like this.

3 Make sure the students understand that each shape must be different. If a shape can be flipped or turned to make another shape, it is not different. Students also need to understand they must use all 5 squares and the blocks should lie flat.

4 Distribute 1-inch grid paper to students. **How many different shapes can you make? Record each shape on your grid paper. When you think you have found all possible arrangements, explain how you know all the shapes are different.**

WHAT SHOULD YOU DO IF . . .

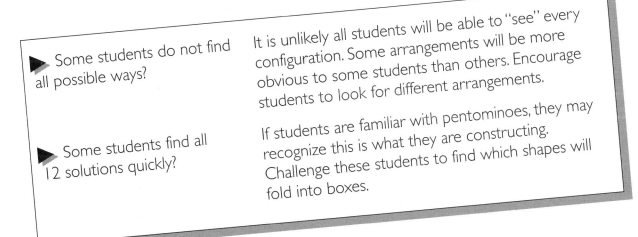

▶ Some students do not find all possible ways?

It is unlikely all students will be able to "see" every configuration. Some arrangements will be more obvious to some students than others. Encourage students to look for different arrangements.

▶ Some students find all 12 solutions quickly?

If students are familiar with pentominoes, they may recognize this is what they are constructing. Challenge these students to find which shapes will fold into boxes.

WHAT YOU MIGHT SEE

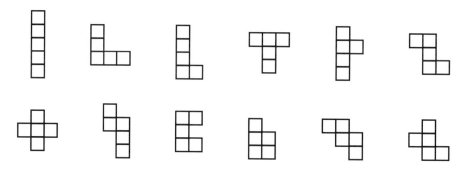

Some students may find all 12 configurations.

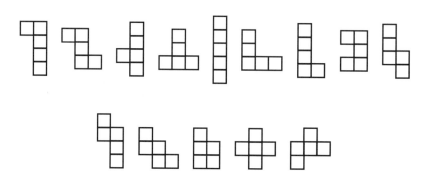

Some students may have 12 or more different shapes but show duplicate shapes.

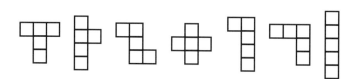

Some students may find fewer than 12 different shapes.

WHAT TO LOOK FOR IN STUDENT'S WORK

Was the student able to find all 12 shapes made with 5 orange squares?

Did the student make a recording of the shapes she found?

Was the student able to explain how he knew all the shapes were different?

QUESTIONS FOR DISCUSSION

- How many different shapes did you make?

- How do you know you found them all?

- Did anyone find more shapes than [Marisa]?

- How did you check to make sure you were not duplicating shapes?

- Are there more or fewer shapes than you thought there would be?

JOURNAL REFLECTION

These shapes are called "pentominoes." Why do you think they are called that?

Do you think your shapes could "fit together" in any way? Explain your thinking.

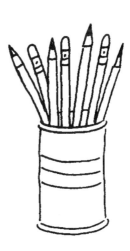

How many different color orders are there?

Use 1 yellow hexagon, 1 blue rhombus, 1 red trapezoid, and 1 green triangle. How many different color orders can you make? Record each way. Explain why you think you have found all the possible orders.

MATERIALS

For each pair of students

- Pattern Blocks (1 yellow, 1 blue, 1 red, and 1 green)
- paper, pencils, and crayons for recording

For the overhead projector

- Pattern Blocks

INTRODUCING THE QUESTION

1 On the overhead projector, show a blue rhombus, a green triangle, and a red trapezoid in a row. **Can you rearrange these blocks to make a different color order?** Show one student's suggestion of a different order.

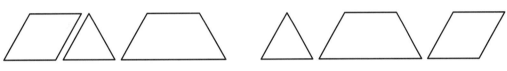

2 Have pairs work with their Pattern Blocks to look for all the different orders. **Do you think there are more ways to rearrange these blocks?** There are 6 different orders.

3 After students have identified the different orders for the 3 blocks, introduce the question. **Suppose there are 4 different blocks. Use I yellow hexagon, I blue rhombus, I red trapezoid, and I green triangle. How many different orders of color do you think there are?** Allow students to make their predictions. **Record each way you find. Explain why you think you have found all the possible orders.**

WHAT SHOULD YOU DO IF . . .

▶ Some students think they have found all possible orders after finding only a few?

Because there are 6 different color orders using 3 blocks, students may not think there are that many more ways with 4 blocks. Without telling students there are 24 different orders, encourage students to continue searching. **How do you know you have found all possible color orders? How can you check?**

▶ Some students find all the different color orders but have difficulty explaining what they did?

Explaining how they found all the possible orders will be difficult for some students, particularly if they have had little experience writing about their thinking. Encourage students to explain their thinking orally and then suggest they write what they just said.

WHAT YOU MIGHT SEE

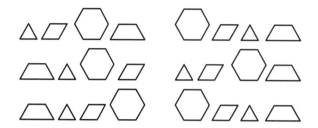

Some students may randomly find ways and duplicate orders of color.

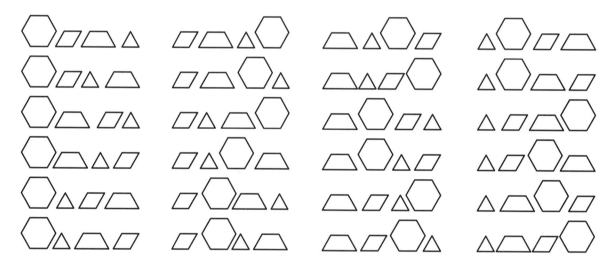

Some students may notice a pattern and organize their work accordingly.

WHAT TO LOOK FOR IN STUDENT'S WORK

Was the student able to find all 24 different color orders of the 4 Pattern Blocks?

Did the student explain clearly how he knows he found all the possible color orders?

QUESTIONS FOR DISCUSSION

- How many different color orders did you find?

- Did you organize your work? If so, in what way?

- Did anyone use another strategy while searching for all the different color orders?

- Did anyone find a different number of orders?

- How did you make sure you didn't count the same order twice?

- How can you be sure you found all the orders possible?

- Are there more color orders with 4 colors than you expected? Explain your thinking.

JOURNAL REFLECTION

Why do you think there are so many more combinations with 4 colors than with 3 colors?

Explain how organizing your work is helpful in problems like these.

QUESTION 4

Can you create a floor pattern?

Suppose the area of a green triangle equals 1. Can you create a floor pattern with an area of 50? Use your Pattern Blocks to create a floor pattern. Then record your floor pattern on Triangle Grid Paper and explain how you determined the area of your floor pattern.

MATERIALS

For each pair of students

- Pattern Blocks
- Triangle Grid Paper (p. 83)
- paper, pencils, and crayons for recording

For the overhead projector

- Pattern Blocks

INTRODUCING THE QUESTION

1 On the overhead projector, show a green triangle. **This green triangle has an area of 1.**

2 Have students select a red trapezoid and cover it with green triangles. **How many triangles did it take to cover the trapezoid?** (3) **What do you think the area of the trapezoid is and why do you think so?**

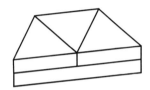

3 Distribute the Triangle Grid Paper to students. **If the area of the green triangle equals 1, can you create a floor pattern with an area of 50? Use your Pattern Blocks to create a floor pattern. Then record your floor pattern on Triangle Grid Paper and explain how you determined the area of your floor pattern.**

4 You may want to have a class tour after everyone has completed their floor designs.

WHAT SHOULD YOU DO IF . . .

▶ Some students are frustrated trying to calculate the area of the tan rhombus and the orange squares?

Knowing that the green triangle is equal to 1 will not help students find the area of these two Pattern Blocks. While it is important that the students come to this realization on their own, you don't want them to spend too much time with this issue. Suggest that they work with the blocks they know the value of to determine the area. Students can talk about any problems they encountered during the class discussion.

▶ Some students are trying to create a floor pattern using only the green triangles?

Ask these students if they can use other Pattern Blocks. **Can you tell me the area of the yellow hexagon? Do you think you could use this block in your floor pattern?**

WHAT YOU MIGHT SEE

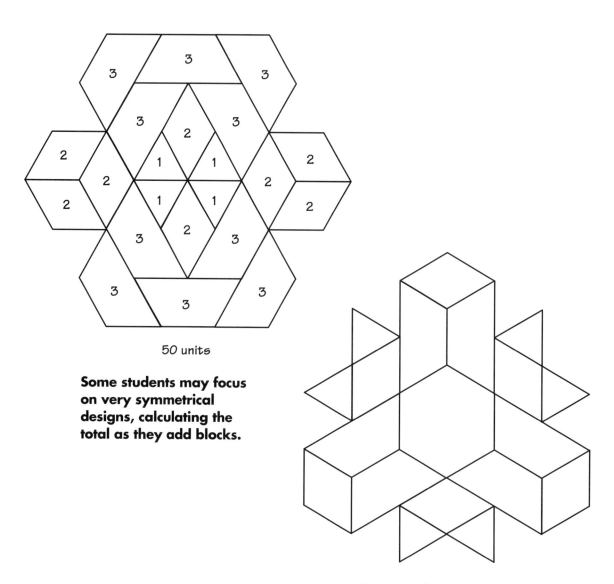

50 units

Some students may focus on very symmetrical designs, calculating the total as they add blocks.

Some students may focus more on the design than on the value of blocks and create a design that is less than or greater than 50.

WHAT TO LOOK FOR IN STUDENT'S WORK

Was the student able to create a floor design with an area of 50?

Did the student explain how he found the area of his floor pattern?

Does the student's work show an understanding of area and the size-relationship of the Pattern Blocks?

QUESTIONS FOR DISCUSSION

- What design did you create? How did you determine the area?

- Did anyone figure the area of their design another way? Tell us about your design.

- Was it easy or difficult for you to make a design with an area of 50? Why do you think so?

- Did you use all the different types of Pattern Blocks in your design? Explain why or why not.

- Did you have any problems determining the area for any of the Pattern Blocks? If so, which blocks?

JOURNAL REFLECTION

How many designs can you create with an area of 50? Explain your thinking.

Suppose you made a floor pattern with an area of 50 using all of one kind of Pattern Block. Of which Pattern Blocks would you use the most? Of which blocks would you use the fewest? Explain your answer.

QUESTION 5

How many shapes are there?

Use 9 green triangles. Make a large triangle using all the blocks. Suppose a small green triangle has an area of 1. How many shapes with an area of 6 can you find in the large triangle? Record each shape you find and explain how you know you have found all the shapes with an area of 6.

MATERIALS

For each pair of students
- Pattern Blocks (9 green)
- paper, pencils, and crayons for recording

For the overhead projector
- Pattern Blocks

INTRODUCING THE QUESTION

1   On the overhead projector, show a large triangle made of 9 green triangles. **If a small green triangle has an area of 1, what is the area of the entire triangle?** (9) **How do you know?**

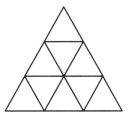

2   **How many shapes with an area of 6 do you think there are in this large triangle?** Allow students to make their predictions.

3   Restate the question for students to solve. **Working with your partner, use 9 triangles and make a large triangle such as on the overhead. If a small green triangle has an area of 1, how many shapes with an area of 6 can you find in the large triangle? Each triangle should be touching at least one side of another triangle.**

4   Have students record their work and explain their thinking. **Record each shape you find and explain how you know you have found all the shapes with an area of 6.**

WHAT SHOULD YOU DO IF . . .

▶ Some students want to know if they have found all the possible ways?

Resist the urge to tell the students whether or not they have found all the ways. It is important for the students to build confidence in themselves and determine whether something is "right" or "wrong." Encourage students to decide for themselves. **Do you think you have found all the shapes with an area of 6? How can you check?**

▶ Some students are disassembling the large triangle to make shapes within an area of 6?

While that is an interesting problem to investigate, these students will get different results than those solving the question as stated. You may simply need to remind the students that the small triangles need to remain in the large triangle configuration.

WHAT YOU MIGHT SEE

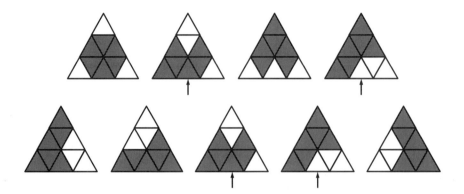

Some students may find most of the shapes with an area of 6 but may duplicate some of the shapes.

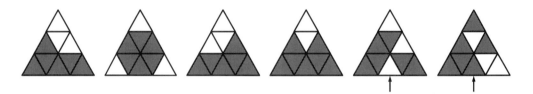

Some students may include shapes where the sides of the triangles are not touching.

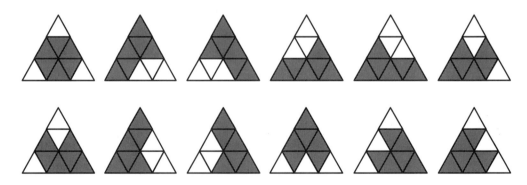

Some students may attempt to organize their work to find all the different shapes.

WHAT TO LOOK FOR IN STUDENT'S WORK

Was the student able to find different shapes with an area of 6?

Did the student make a recording of his work?

Was the student able to explain why he thought he had found all the different shapes with an area of 6?

QUESTIONS FOR DISCUSSION

- How many different shapes with an area of 6 did you find?

- Did anyone find a different number of shapes?

- Do you think you found all the shapes that have an area of 6? Why or why not?

- How did you make sure you weren't making the same shape twice?

- Did you think there would be more or fewer shapes with an area of 6?

JOURNAL REFLECTION

Suppose the question was to find the shapes with an area of 5. Do you think there would be more or fewer shapes? Explain why you think so.

If you asked a family member today's question, do you think they would be able to find all the shapes with an area of 6? Explain your answer.

6 What are the least and greatest number of blocks needed?

What is the least number of blocks you would need to cover this spaceship? What is the greatest number of blocks? Use your Pattern Blocks to help find the answers. Then record your work and explain how you determined the least and greatest number of blocks needed.

MATERIALS

For each pair of students

■ Pattern Blocks
■ Spaceship reproducible (p. 84)
■ paper, pencils, and crayons for recording

For the overhead projector

■ Pattern Blocks

INTRODUCING THE QUESTION

1 Trace an outline of a yellow hexagon on the overhead projector.
Can you cover this shape using different Pattern Blocks?
Have students share several different ways to cover the hexagon.

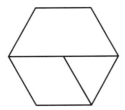

2 Pass out the Spaceship reproducible to each pair of students and
introduce the question. **Can you cover this shape using your
Pattern Blocks? What is the least number of blocks you will
need to cover this spaceship? What is the greatest number
of blocks?**

3 **Record your work and explain how you determined the least
and greatest number of blocks you would need to cover the
spaceship.**

WHAT SHOULD YOU DO IF . . .

▶ Some students are not using the yellow hexagons when finding the least number of blocks?

▶ Some pairs are combining or sharing their blocks?

These students may not have a clear understanding of the concept that the larger blocks cover more area. Rather than tell them, let them come to this realization on their own.

Some students may realize that the green triangles will render the greatest number of blocks needed. They may also discover they don't have enough green triangles and are sharing to find the solution.

WHAT YOU MIGHT SEE

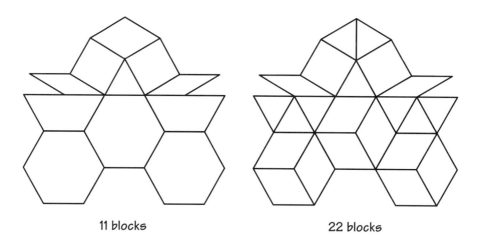

11 blocks   22 blocks

Some students may find the least and greatest number of blocks needed using the blocks they have.

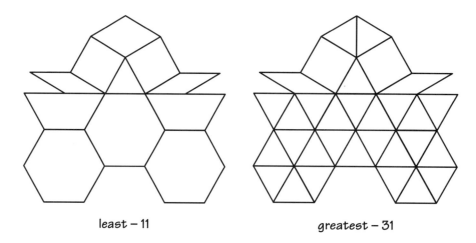

least – 11   greatest – 31

Some students may figure the least and greatest number of blocks needed based on their understanding of area.

WHAT TO LOOK FOR IN STUDENT'S WORK

Was the student able to determine the least and greatest number of blocks needed to cover the spaceship?

Was the student able to explain how he determined the least and greatest number of blocks needed to cover the spaceship?

Does the student's work show an understanding of the relationship among the Pattern Blocks?

QUESTIONS FOR DISCUSSION

- What was the least number of blocks you found to cover the spaceship? What blocks did you use?

- Did anyone find a way using fewer blocks? What blocks did you use?

- What was the greatest number of blocks you found to cover the spaceship? What blocks did you use?

- Did anyone find another way to cover the spaceship? Did you use more or fewer blocks?

- Did you use all the different types of Pattern Blocks in your set? Explain your answer.

JOURNAL REFLECTION

If you were going to cover the yellow hexagon with the greatest number of Pattern Blocks, what block(s) would you use and why?

Which was easier to determine, the least or greatest number of blocks it took to cover the spaceship? Explain your thinking.

Was it helpful to work with a partner on this question? Explain why or why not.

QUESTION 7

Can you make a design that has 1 line of symmetry?

Use 12 Pattern Blocks. Can you make a design that has 1 line of symmetry? Record your design. Write about how you know your design is symmetrical.

MATERIALS

For each pair of students
- Pattern Blocks
- paper, pencils, and crayons for recording

For the overhead projector
- Pattern Blocks

INTRODUCING THE QUESTION

1   Show a blue rhombus on the overhead projector. **Can you divide this rhombus so that two halves are mirror images of each other?** Have students show you how to divide the block.

2   Discuss the meaning of symmetry with your students. **Point to the line dividing the block. We call this the *line of symmetry*. How many lines of symmetry can you find in the blue rhombus?** (2)

3   On the overhead projector, add 2 green triangles to the blue rhombus. **Can you divide this design so that 2 sides are mirror images of each other? How many lines of symmetry can you find?** (1) Make sure your students understand they are not physically dividing the blocks but rather are finding an imaginary line that creates mirror images.

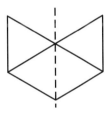

4   Introduce the question to the class. **Use 12 Pattern Blocks. Can you make a design that has 1 line of symmetry? Record your design. Write about how you know there is 1 line of symmetry.**

WHAT SHOULD YOU DO IF . . .

▶ Some students think they have to separate the blocks physically in order to show a line of symmetry?

Some students may need to separate the design in order to "see" the line of symmetry. Eventually they should realize they can find an imaginary line and not feel the need to separate the blocks.

▶ Some students want to use more than 12 blocks to create their design?

In general, the larger the design, the more difficult it is to maintain a line of symmetry. These students may want to build an elaborate design as a challenge.

WHAT YOU MIGHT SEE

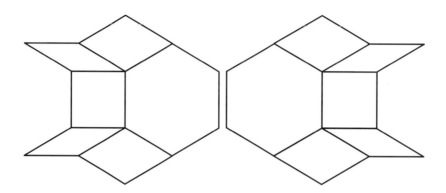

Some students may separate the blocks to identify the line of symmetry in their design.

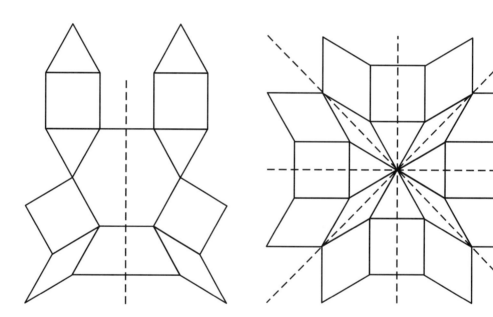

Some students may create a design using 12 Pattern Blocks and identify the line of symmetry as an imaginary line.

Some students may create and identify a design with more than one line of symmetry.

WHAT TO LOOK FOR IN STUDENT'S WORK

Was the student able to create a design with 1 line of symmetry using 12 Pattern Blocks?

Was the student able to identify the line of symmetry?

Does the student's explanation show a clear understanding of symmetry?

QUESTIONS FOR DISCUSSION

■ Who can describe a design and tell us where the line of symmetry is? How did you decide where the line of symmetry belongs?

■ Would anyone else like to share a design? Is the line of symmetry for your design horizontal or vertical?

■ Did anyone create a design that has a [vertical] line of symmetry? Did anyone create a design with a diagonal line of symmetry? What does your design look like?

■ How many blocks are in your design? Did creating a design with 12 Pattern Blocks make it easier or more difficult? Why do you think so?

■ Does your design have more than 1 line of symmetry? How many lines of symmetry does it have? How do you know?

■ How would you describe *symmetry*?

JOURNAL REFLECTION

When someone describes a symmetrical object, what do you think he means?

What are some things you see around you that are symmetrical? (These can also be things you remember.)

What blocks are worth $1.56?

Suppose the yellow hexagon equals $0.18. What blocks could you use to build a design worth $1.56? Use 15 or more Pattern Blocks to create your design. Then record your design and write how you know it is worth $1.56.

MATERIALS

For each pair of students

■ Pattern Blocks
■ paper, pencils, and crayons for recording

For the overhead projector

■ Pattern Blocks

INTRODUCING THE QUESTION

1 On the overhead projector, show 6 red trapezoids encircling a yellow hexagon. If the yellow hexagon is worth 10¢, what is the entire design worth? (40¢) **How did you figure how much each red block is worth?** Allow students to respond, listening for more than one way to figure the value.

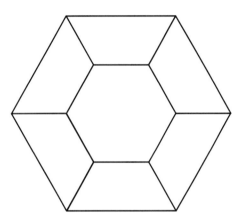

2 Introduce students to today's challenge. **Suppose the yellow hexagon equals $0.18. What blocks could you use to build a design worth $1.56? Use 15 or more Pattern Blocks. Record your design and write how you know it is worth $1.56.**

WHAT SHOULD YOU DO IF . . .

▶ Some students think the problem is too easy?

Finding the value of the red, blue, and green Pattern Blocks should not be difficult for the students. However, finding a combination of at least 15 blocks that equals $1.56 should prove a bit more challenging. If students do finish quickly, change the value of the hexagon or suggest they find more than one way to show $1.56.

▶ Some students make a design using fewer than 15 blocks?

These students may be trying to use as many yellow hexagons as possible and forget that their design should have at least 15 blocks. Ask students to restate the question and check their work to be sure it is an acceptable solution.

WHAT YOU MIGHT SEE

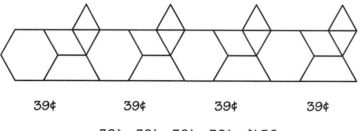

| 39¢ | 39¢ | 39¢ | 39¢ |

39¢ + 39¢ + 39¢ + 39¢ = $1.56

Some students may determine the value for a section of a pattern and repeat it until the total is $1.56.

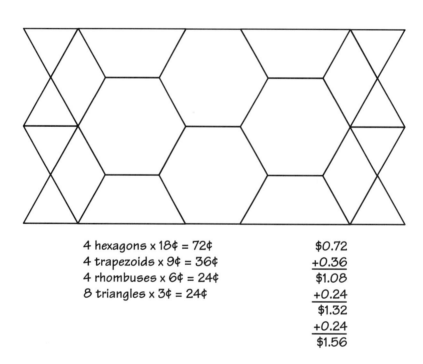

4 hexagons x 18¢ = 72¢ $0.72
4 trapezoids x 9¢ = 36¢   +0.36
4 rhombuses x 6¢ = 24¢ $1.08
8 triangles x 3¢ = 24¢   +0.24
                                      $1.32
                                   +0.24
                                   $1.56

Some students may create a design and calculate the total as they add to the design.

WHAT TO LOOK FOR IN STUDENT'S WORK

Was the student able to create a design with a value of $1.56?

Was the student able to explain how he calculated the value of his design?

QUESTIONS FOR DISCUSSION

- What design did you create with a value of $1.56? How did you figure the value?

- Who created a different design? How did you figure the value of your design?

- Did anyone use a different strategy for figuring the value of a design?

- How many blocks did you use to create your design?

- Did anyone create more than one design?

- Which blocks did you use most frequently? Why do you think that was?

JOURNAL REFLECTION

Can you create a design that has fewer than 15 blocks and still have a value of $1.56? Why or why not?

What do you think is the fewest blocks you could use to create a design with a value of $1.56 when a hexagon equals $0.18?

Do you think you could find all the possible ways to make a design worth $1.56? Explain why or why not.

QUESTION 9

Can you make a design with an area of 17?

Suppose the area of a yellow hexagon equals 3. Can you make a design with an area of 17? Record your design. Explain how you figured the area.

MATERIALS

For each pair of students
- Pattern Blocks
- paper, pencils, and crayons for recording

For the overhead projector
- Pattern Blocks

INTRODUCING THE QUESTION

1   Show a yellow hexagon on the overhead projector. **If this hexagon has an area of 6, can you figure the area of the red trapezoid?** (3) **How do you know? Can you find the area of the blue rhombus?** (2) Have students explain how they figured the area.

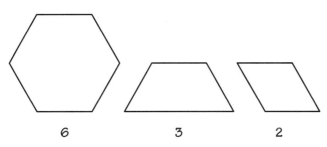

        6   3   2

2   Show the yellow hexagon on the overhead projector again. **If this hexagon has an area of 3, can you figure the area of the red trapezoid?** ($1\frac{1}{2}$) **How do you know? Why is the area different than before?** Allow students to give their reasons.

3   Introduce the question to the class. **If the yellow hexagon has an area of 3, can you make a shape, pattern, or design with an area of 17? Record your design. Explain how you figured the area for your design.**

WHAT SHOULD YOU DO IF . . .

▶ Some students are using the orange squares and tan rhombuses in their design?

▶ Some students are concentrating on the design or pattern and not on finding an area of 17?

Given the area of the hexagon, students can't calculate the area of the orange square and tan rhombus. Ask the students how they figured the area for these blocks.

If the students are involved with their patterns, you may decide to let them design to their hearts' content. Just stipulate that they must complete the problem. **You still must figure the area of your designs.**

WHAT YOU MIGHT SEE

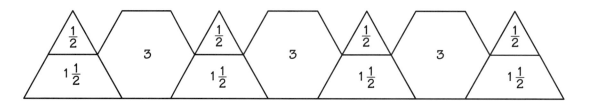

Some students may create a pattern with an area of 17.

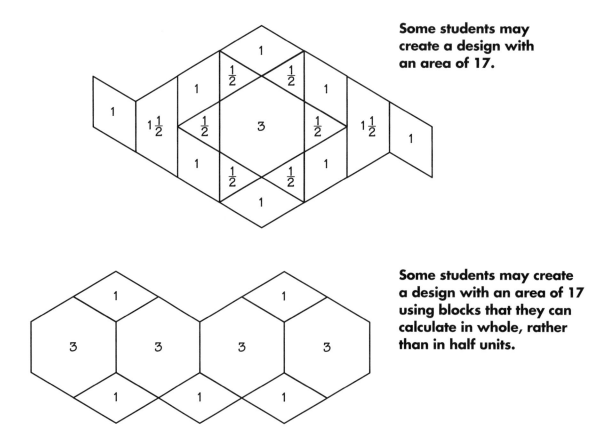

Some students may create a design with an area of 17.

Some students may create a design with an area of 17 using blocks that they can calculate in whole, rather than in half units.

WHAT TO LOOK FOR IN STUDENT'S WORK

Was the student able to create at least one design with an area of 17?

Did the student's explanation clearly show how she figured the area?

Does the student's work show his understanding of the size relationship of the Pattern Blocks?

QUESTIONS FOR DISCUSSION

- Describe what design you created with an area of 17. How did you figure the area?

- Was creating a design with an area of exactly 17 difficult for you? Why or why not?

- Did you create more than one design or pattern?

- Did anyone create a different pattern, design, or shape? Did it have an area of 17? How do you know?

- How many different designs or patterns do you think you could create with an area of 17?

- How did you figure the area for each of the Pattern Blocks?

- Which pattern blocks were the easiest to figure the area? Why?

JOURNAL REFLECTION

Do you think you could create many designs, patterns, or shapes that have an area of 25? Explain your thinking.

Do you think there are more or fewer ways to create a design, pattern, or shape with an area of 17 or 25? Explain your reasoning.

Can you make a design, pattern, or shape using only yellow or blue blocks that has an area of $11\frac{1}{2}$? Explain your answer.

Can you find the greatest and the least perimeter?

Use 4 yellow hexagons and 6 red trapezoids.
Using these 10 blocks, can you find the greatest
and the least perimeter? Record your work.
Explain how you know you have found the greatest
and the least perimeter.

MATERIALS

For each pair of students

- Pattern Blocks (4 yellow, 6 red)
- paper, pencils, and crayons for recording

For the overhead projector

- Pattern Blocks

INTRODUCING THE QUESTION

1   On the overhead projector, show a yellow hexagon and point to one side. **If the length of this side is 1 unit, what is the perimeter of this block?** (6 units) Show a red trapezoid on the overhead. **What is the perimeter of this block?** (5 units) **How do you know?** Allow students to give explanations. Be sure students understand they need to count the long side as 2 units.

2   Put a hexagon and a trapezoid together so the sides are touching. Ask students to find the perimeter of the shape (9 units) and tell how they figured the perimeter. Then show on the overhead examples of the acceptable and not acceptable ways to put pattern blocks together.

Acceptable   Not Acceptable

3   Introduce the question to the class. **Use 4 yellow hexagons and 6 red trapezoids. Use all the blocks to create a shape. Can you find the greatest and the least perimeter? Record your work and explain how you know you have found the greatest and the least perimeter.**

WHAT SHOULD YOU DO IF . . .

► Some students are having difficulty counting the perimeter?

The angles of the Pattern Blocks may make it difficult for some student to remember which sides they have already counted. Some students may forget to count the long side of the red trapezoid as 2 units. If counting the long side as 2 units is difficult for students, suggest exchanging the 6 red trapezoids for 9 blue parallelograms.

► Some students find the greatest perimeter of 36 units and yet continue to search?

These students are most likely *not* convinced they have found the greatest perimeter. It's important for students to come to this conclusion on their own. Let them continue to search!

WHAT YOU MIGHT SEE

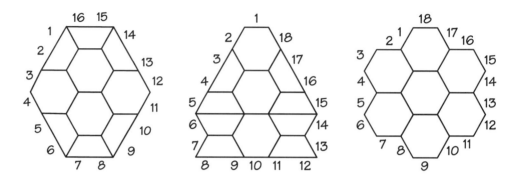

Some students may find several ways to show the least (or greatest) perimeter.

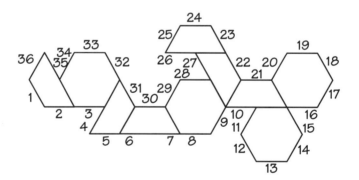

Some students may create a shape with the greatest (or least) perimeter but miscalculate the perimeter.

Some students may try to make the greatest perimeter by making lots of "nooks and crannies."

WHAT TO LOOK FOR IN STUDENT'S WORK

Was the student able to find the greatest (36 units) and the least (16 units) perimeters?

Was the student able to explain clearly how he found the greatest or the least perimeter?

QUESTIONS FOR DISCUSSION

- What was the greatest perimeter you found? What does your shape look like?

- How did you figure the perimeter?

- Did anyone find a perimeter greater than [student's name]? Do you think this is the greatest perimeter? How do you know you can't find a shape with a greater perimeter?

- What was the least perimeter you found?

- Did anyone find a perimeter less than that?

- Did you find different shapes that had the same perimeter?

- Which was more difficult, finding the greatest or the least perimeter? Why?

JOURNAL REFLECTION

What did you notice about the difference between the shape with the greatest perimeter and the shape with the least perimeter?

Why do you think different shapes can have the same perimeter?

11 How many fractions can you find?

Use your Pattern Blocks to find as many ways as you can to show a hexagon. What fraction does each Pattern Block show? Record your work and label the fractions you find. Write an addition sentence for each hexagon you make.

MATERIALS

For each pair of students

- Pattern Blocks
- paper, pencils, and crayons for recording

For the overhead projector

- Pattern Blocks

INTRODUCING THE QUESTION

1 On the overhead projector, show the yellow hexagon. **Can you cover this hexagon with trapezoids?**

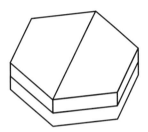

2 If the hexagon is 1 whole, what fraction of the whole is the trapezoid? $\left(\frac{1}{2}\right)$ How do you know? Are there other blocks you can use to show the hexagon?

3 Tell students they will be looking for other ways to show a hexagon and name the fractions they find. **How many ways can you show a hexagon with the other Pattern Blocks? What fraction does each Pattern Block show? Record your work and label the fractions you find. Write an addition sentence for each hexagon you make.**

WHAT SHOULD YOU DO IF . . .

▶ Some students make hexagons using only one type of block?

These students may not think about using different kinds of blocks or they may be constructing only the fractions they can name. This may tell you a great deal about what your students know about fractions. Encourage students to look for other ways of combining the blocks. **Can you find a way to make a hexagon using different blocks? Can you name the fractions?**

▶ Some students find and label their fractions quickly?

Students with a good understanding of fractions may find and name fractional parts for all their Pattern Blocks. It may be more of a challenge for them to discuss why the green triangle is $\frac{1}{6}$ of the yellow hexagon and $\frac{1}{2}$ of the blue rhombus.

WHAT YOU MIGHT SEE

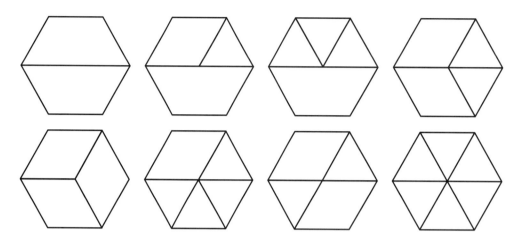

Some students may find all the different ways to show a hexagon but are unable to label each fractional part.

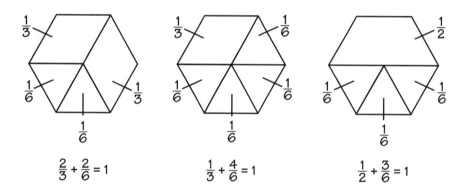

$\frac{2}{3} + \frac{2}{6} = 1$ $\frac{1}{3} + \frac{4}{6} = 1$ $\frac{1}{2} + \frac{3}{6} = 1$

Some students may label each fractional part and then group the "like" fractions together when writing the addition sentence.

WHAT TO LOOK FOR IN STUDENT'S WORK

Was the student able to show and label several examples of fractional parts of a hexagon?

Does the student's work show an understanding of fractions?

Was the student able to write an addition sentence for each way she represented a hexagon?

QUESTIONS FOR DISCUSSION

- How many hexagons were you able to make? What are the fractions you found?

- Did anyone find any different fractions?

- How did you know what to label each fraction?

- Were some fractions easier than others to determine? Why do you think so?

- Are there any blocks you didn't use to show fractional parts of a hexagon? Why do you think they didn't work?

- Do you think the class found all the possible ways to show fractions using the hexagon? Why or why not?

JOURNAL REFLECTION

Is the orange square a fractional part of the yellow hexagon? Can you determine what that fraction is? Why or why not?

Can you divide a hexagon into fourths using your Pattern blocks? Explain why or why not.

QUESTION 12

Can you make a design where $\frac{1}{4}$ of the area is green?

Can you make a design or pattern where $\frac{1}{4}$ of the area is green? Use your Pattern Blocks to make a design. Then record your design and explain how you know that $\frac{1}{4}$ of the area is green.

MATERIALS

For each pair of students

- Pattern Blocks (9 red, 9 blue, 9 green, and 4 yellow)
- paper, pencils, and crayons for recording

For the overhead projector

- Pattern Blocks

INTRODUCING THE QUESTION

1 On the overhead projector, show a green block. **This green triangle has an area of 1. If you know the area of the green triangle is 1, can you figure the area of the red trapezoid?** (3) **How do you know?**

2 On the overhead projector, show a design with a red trapezoid, a blue rhombus, and a green triangle. **What is the area of this design?** (6) **How did you figure the area?**

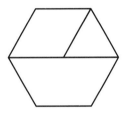

3 Discuss with students the fractional value of each block in the design. **What is the area of the red trapezoid?** (3) **If you know the area of the whole design is 6 and the area of the trapezoid is 3, what fraction of the area of the whole design is red?** ($\frac{3}{6}$ or $\frac{1}{2}$) **What fraction of the area of the design do you think is green?** ($\frac{1}{6}$) Show additional examples if needed.

4 Challenge students to work with their partner and to find designs where $\frac{1}{4}$ of the area is green. **Can you create designs where $\frac{1}{4}$ of the area is green? Make a recording of your design and explain how you know $\frac{1}{4}$ of the area is green.**

WHAT SHOULD YOU DO IF . . .

▶ Some students are making designs where $\frac{1}{4}$ of the area is not green?

Have students focus on one aspect of the question at a time. **What is the area of your green blocks? Of your red blocks? What is the total area? What part of the whole design is green?**

▶ Some students are creating the same design?

That's fine. It's more important that the students are able to explain how the area is $\frac{1}{4}$ green than to create an original design. You may also want to encourage these students to make a design that no one else has discovered.

WHAT YOU MIGHT SEE

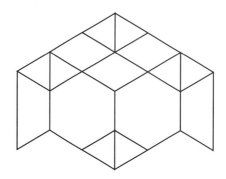

Some students may make elaborate designs where $\frac{1}{4}$ of the area is green.

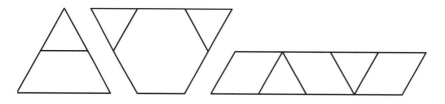

Some students may make several simple designs where $\frac{1}{4}$ of the area is green.

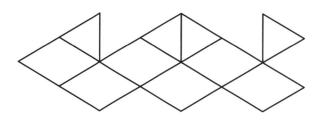

Some students may look for patterns divisible by 4 to help them determine what $\frac{1}{4}$ of the area would be.

WHAT TO LOOK FOR IN STUDENT'S WORK

Did the student create a design where $\frac{1}{4}$ of the area is green?

Does the student's explanation relate an understanding of fractions?

Was the student able to explain clearly how he figured the area of his design?

QUESTIONS FOR DISCUSSION

- What does your design look like?

- How do you know $\frac{1}{4}$ of the area is green?

- Did anyone find another design where the area is $\frac{1}{4}$ green?

- How did you decide which Pattern Blocks to use in your design?

- What strategies did you use to find $\frac{1}{4}$ of the area?

- Did anyone use other Pattern Blocks in their design?

- Which Pattern Blocks did you use the most in your design?

- Can you name any of the other fractions in your design?

JOURNAL REFLECTION

What Pattern Blocks did you notice being used most frequently? Why do you think that was?

How would you explain $\frac{1}{4}$ to a friend?

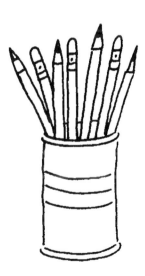

QUESTION 13

What is the measurement of the angles?

What is the measurement of each angle in your set of Pattern Blocks? Record your work and write how you figured the measurement of each angle.

MATERIALS

For each pair of students

■   Pattern Blocks
■   paper, pencils, and crayons for recording

For the overhead projector

■   Pattern Blocks

INTRODUCING THE QUESTION

1 On the overhead projector, show a green triangle. **This is an equilateral triangle.** Elicit the meaning of an equilateral triangle from students.

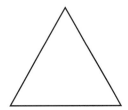

Equilateral triangle: a triangle with sides of equal length and with each angle measuring 60°

2 **Suppose you know all the sides and angles are equal and the total of all the angles in a triangle is 180°. Can you determine the measurement for each angle of the green triangle?** (60°) **How did you find the measurement for each angle?** Have students share their explanations.

3 With a partner, have the students find the measurement for all the angles. **What is the measurement of each angle in your set of Pattern Blocks? Keep a record and explain how you know the measurement of each angle.**

WHAT SHOULD YOU DO IF . . .

► Some students are having difficulty finding the measurements of the angles for the tan rhombus and the orange square?

These two Pattern Blocks will be the most difficult for the students to figure, though it can be done. Many students may know a square has four right angles that are 90° each. Suggest to students that they "prove" the measurement of each angle using different blocks. For the tan rhombus, suggest to students that they use different combinations of blocks to measure each angle.

► Some students find the measurements of all the angles before the rest of the class has finished?

You may want to have students who finish early create a shape and then measure the angles for their shape. They could also determine the total for all the angles of the shape.

WHAT YOU MIGHT SEE

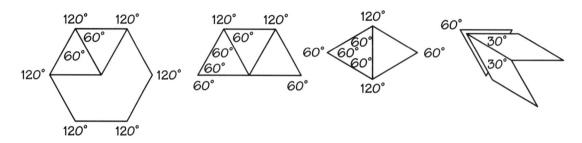

Some students may find the measurement of all the angles using only the triangle to help measure each angle.

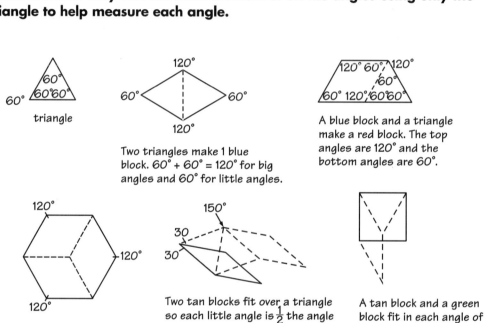

triangle

Two triangles make 1 blue block. 60° + 60° = 120° for big angles and 60° for little angles.

A blue block and a triangle make a red block. The top angles are 120° and the bottom angles are 60°.

A blue block fits every angle in hexagon so each angle is 120°.

Two tan blocks fit over a triangle so each little angle is $\frac{1}{2}$ the angle of the triangle = 30°. The big angle is two triangles and a tan block. 60° + 60° = 120° + 30° = 150°

A tan block and a green block fit in each angle of the orange block. Each angle in the square is 90° (60° + 30°).

Some students may use angles in other Pattern Blocks besides the triangle to determine the measurement of different angles.

WHAT TO LOOK FOR IN STUDENT'S WORK

Was the student able to determine the measurement for each angle in the set of Pattern Blocks?

Did the student clearly explain how he determined the measurements for each angle?

Does the student's work explain how she used Pattern Blocks to determine the measurement of the angles?

QUESTIONS FOR DISCUSSION

- What are the measurements for the different angles you found? How did you figure the measurement for each angle?

- Did anyone find the measurements in a different way? How?

- Which Pattern Block did you use more than the others to determine the different angles? Why do you think you used it more frequently?

- Were some angles more difficult to measure than others? Why do you think so?

- Which measurement did you find most frequently?

JOURNAL REFLECTION

Design a new Pattern Block and figure the measurement for each angle.

Why do you think the Pattern Blocks fit together the way they do?

14

Which of these shapes can you make?

Using the green triangles, which of these shapes can you make: square, rectangle, triangle, trapezoid, parallelogram, hexagon, pentagon, or circle? Make a recording of the shapes you can make. Can you make all the shapes? If not, write why you think you are able to make some shapes and unable to make other shapes.

MATERIALS

For each pair of students

- Pattern Blocks (9 green)
- paper, pencils, and crayons for recording

INTRODUCING THE QUESTION

1 Discuss the meanings of the following shapes: square, rectangle, triangle, trapezoid, parallelogram, hexagon, pentagon, and circle. **Who can describe a square? Can anyone think of an example of a square?**

2 Continue discussing all the shapes in this fashion. Write the students' definitions of the shapes on the chalkboard for them to refer to while solving the question.

3 Introduce students to the question. **Use the green triangles. Which of these shapes can you make: square, rectangle, triangle, trapezoid, parallelogram, hexagon, pentagon, or circle?** Ask students if they have any guesses before beginning.

4 **Work with your partner and make a recording of the shapes you can make. Can you make all the shapes? If not, write why you think you are able to make some of the shapes and unable to make other shapes.**

WHAT SHOULD YOU DO IF . . .

▶ Some pairs seem to be "arguing" about whether or not they can make a shape?

It is good for students to disagree and be able to explain their thinking to others. The pentagon may bring about the most discourse. Some students may feel they cannot make a pentagon because it is not a regular pentagon, and their partner may argue that as long as it has 5 sides, it's a pentagon. Try to refrain from intervening; it's important that students learn to figure this out for themselves.

▶ Some students think they must use all 9 green triangles to make their shapes?

Let students challenge themselves. **You may use as few or as many triangles as you need to make your shapes.**

WHAT YOU MIGHT SEE

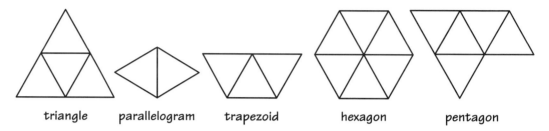

triangle   parallelogram   trapezoid   hexagon   pentagon

Some students may find they can make all the shapes except the square, the rectangle, and the circle.

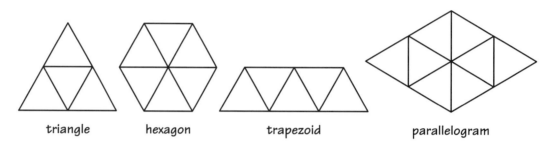

triangle   hexagon   trapezoid   parallelogram

Some students may find most of the shapes.

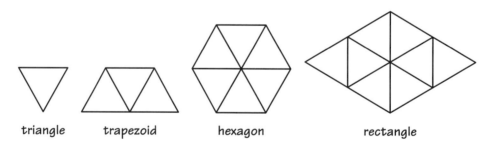

triangle   trapezoid   hexagon   rectangle

Some students may mislabel a parallelogram as a rectangle.

WHAT TO LOOK FOR IN STUDENT'S WORK

Was the student able to make most of the shapes using the green triangles?

Does the student's explanation clearly state why she could make some shapes and not others?

QUESTIONS FOR DISCUSSION

- How many shapes were you able to make with your triangles?

- Which shapes were you able to make?

- Did anyone find another shape that we haven't mentioned yet?

- Were there any shapes that you were unable to make? Why do you think so?

- If you had more triangles, do you think you would be able to make these shapes? Explain your thinking.

- Which shape was the most difficult to make? Why do you think so?

JOURNAL REFLECTION

Explain what you learned about shapes today.

Why is a square impossible to make using only triangles?

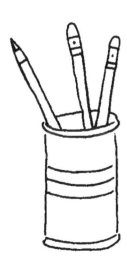

QUESTION 15

What color is the hundredth block?

Use your Pattern Blocks to make this pattern: red, red, green, red, red, green. Suppose you continued the pattern. What color would the hundredth block be? Make a recording that explains how you know what the hundredth block would be.

MATERIALS

For each pair of students

- Pattern Blocks (red and green)
- paper, pencils, and crayons for recording

For the overhead projector

- Pattern Blocks

INTRODUCING THE QUESTION

1 Show the following pattern on the overhead projector: red trapezoid, red trapezoid, green triangle, red trapezoid, red trapezoid, green triangle. **If this pattern continued, do you know what color the hundredth block would be?**

2 **Do you have enough blocks to solve this question with your partner?** (no) **Work with your partner. Think of another method for figuring out what the hundredth block would be.**

3 **Record your work and explain your method for figuring what color the hundredth block would be.**

WHAT SHOULD YOU DO IF . . .

▶ Some students solve the question quickly?

If some pairs finish before the rest of the class, challenge these students to find how many green and how many red blocks it would take to make the pattern to 100 blocks.

▶ Some students want to know if they have the right answer when they are finished?

These students may not be convinced their answer is correct. Encourage them to come to this conclusion on their own. **Do you think it is correct? Why do you think so? Can you explain why you think it is right?**

WHAT YOU MIGHT SEE

3 blocks in each section
3 x 30 sections = 90 blocks

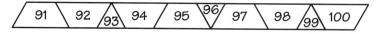

100th block is red.

Some students may figure a formula for determining the color of the hundredth block.

red	green
1, 2	3
4, 5	6
7, 8	9
10, 11	12
13, 14	15
16, 17	18
19, 20	21
22, 23	24
25, 26	27
28, 29	30
31, 32	33

Some students may make a chart to determine the color of the hundredth block.

WHAT TO LOOK FOR IN STUDENT'S WORK

Was the student able to determine that the color of the hundredth block would be red?

Did the student explain her method for finding the color of the hundredth block?

QUESTIONS FOR DISCUSSION

■ What color do you think the hundredth block would be? What strategy did you use to determine this?

■ Did anyone use another strategy to figure the hundredth block?

■ Does anyone think it is a different color block?

■ Did anyone count how many red and how many green blocks there are in this pattern? Do you think that will be easy or difficult to figure? Explain your thinking.

JOURNAL REFLECTION

Could you use your same strategy to determine what the two hundredth block would be? Explain your reasoning.

Is there more than one way to solve this problem? Explain your thinking.

QUESTION 16

How many layers will you need?

Arrange your Pattern Blocks like a star (yellow hexagon in the middle and 6 triangles around the outside). Suppose a green triangle equals 1. How many layers of stars will you need to equal 105? Record your work and explain how you found your solution.

MATERIALS

For each pair of students

- Pattern Blocks (yellow and green)
- paper, pencils, and crayons for recording

For the overhead projector

- Pattern Blocks

INTRODUCING THE QUESTION

1 On the overhead projector, show a red trapezoid surrounded by 4 green triangles. **Suppose the green triangle equals 1 and the red trapezoid equals 3. What is the value of this design?** (7) **How do you know?**

2 **Suppose there were 2 designs. What would the value be?** (14). **How many designs would you need to show a value of 28?** (4)

3 On the overhead, show a star as described and introduce today's question. **Use your Pattern Blocks and build a star like the one on the overhead. If the green triangle equals 1, how many layers of stars will you need to equal 105?**

4 Have students record their work and explain how they figured their solutions.

WHAT SHOULD YOU DO IF . . .

▶ Some students are not considering the value of the yellow hexagon when figuring their solutions?

Because the yellow hexagon was not mentioned in the question, students may forget to figure its value. Remind students they have another block in the design. **What about the yellow hexagon? Can you figure its value?**

▶ Some pairs seem to disagree about the number of layers needed?

How students interpret the question affects how they respond. Some students may think they should be finding the exact value of 105, hence making partial layers. Other students may think the design can't be broken and should be solved with complete layers. It will be interesting to see how students resolve this issue themselves. Another good time to discuss the matter will be during the class discussion.

WHAT YOU MIGHT SEE

1 star = 12   6 stars = 72
2 stars = 24   7 stars = 84
3 stars = 36   8 stars = 96
4 stars = 48   9 stars = 108
5 stars = 60

Some students may make a chart and determine that they need 9 layers of stars to equal 105.

```
1    12          84
2   +12      8  +12
    ───          ───
     24           96
3   +12          +9
    ───          ───
     36          105
4   +12
    ───
     48
5   +12
    ───
     60
6   +12
    ───
     72
7   +12                  8 layers of stars
    ───          and 1 yellow hexagon and 3 green triangles
     84
```

Some students may determine that a partial layer of stars is needed to equal 105 exactly.

  · · ·

6 + 6 = 12   24   · · ·   96   105

Some students may draw the stars to determine the number of whole and partial layers they will need.

WHAT TO LOOK FOR IN STUDENT'S WORK

Was the student able to determine the number of whole and partial layers of stars needed to equal 105?

Was the student able to explain her strategy for figuring the number of whole and partial layers of stars?

QUESTIONS FOR DISCUSSION

- How many layers of stars did you need to make 105? How did you figure the number of layers?

- Did anyone use a different strategy to solve the problem?

- Did anyone figure a different number of layers? How did you solve the problem?

- Did you have enough Pattern Blocks to solve this question? How did you check your answer?

- Does it make a difference whether you make complete or partial layers? Explain your thinking.

- Did anyone try a strategy and find it didn't work? What did you do then?

JOURNAL REFLECTION

Does it make a difference whether you make complete or partial layers of stars to equal 105? Explain your thinking.

Did using the Pattern Blocks make it easier or more difficult to solve this problem? Explain your thinking.

17 How many growing triangles can you make?

Use the green triangles. Build the next larger and the next larger triangle as far as you can. When you run out of Pattern Blocks, draw on grid paper. If you had 50 triangles, how many growing triangles could you make? Make a recording and write about any patterns you see.

MATERIALS

For each pair of students

- Pattern Blocks (green)
- paper, pencils, and crayons for recording
- Triangle Grid Paper (p. 83)

For the overhead projector

- Pattern Blocks

INTRODUCING THE QUESTION

1 On the overhead projector, show 1 orange square. **This is a square using 1 block. With your partner, use your Pattern Blocks to make the next larger square. How many blocks did you use?** (4)

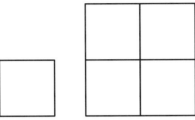

2 Introduce the question to the class. **Today we will be looking at growing shapes. Use the green triangles. Build the next larger and the next larger triangle. If you had 50 green triangles, how many growing triangles could you make? When you run out of triangles, use grid paper.** Explain to students that they can reuse triangles to build the next larger triangle.

3 **Keep a recording of the triangles you make. Also record the number of blocks in each growing triangle and the number of blocks you add to each growing triangle. Write about any patterns you see.**

WHAT SHOULD YOU DO IF . . .

▶ Some students don't seem to know what to do or where to begin?

Understanding the directions for this question can be tricky. Placing the directions somewhere in the classroom for the students to refer to may alleviate some of the confusion.

▶ Some students "see" the pattern before they have built as many growing triangles as they can with 50 green triangles?

These students may recognize the squaring pattern early on and can predict the outcome. Great! Encourage these students to confirm their predictions and suggest they look for patterns with growing shapes of other Pattern Blocks.

WHAT YOU MIGHT SEE

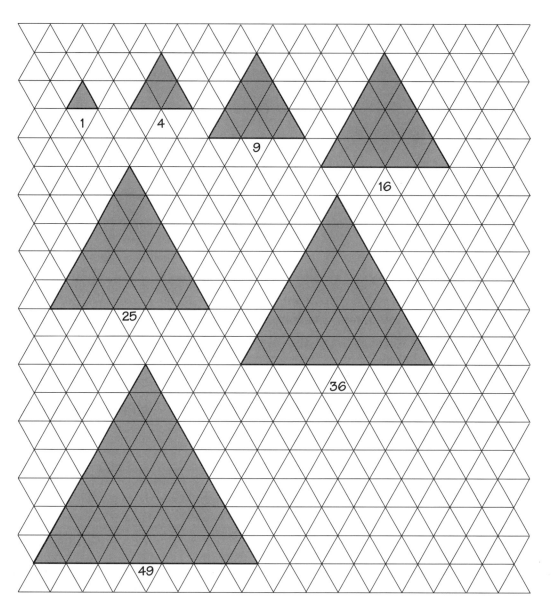

Some students may draw or record on grid paper a series of growing triangles to determine how many they can make with 50 triangles. Other students may create a chart to determine the number of growing triangles.

WHAT TO LOOK FOR IN STUDENT'S WORK

Was the student able to build and draw a growing progression of triangles?

Does the student's explanation describe the patterns or relationships she noticed?

QUESTIONS FOR DISCUSSION

- How many growing triangles can you make if you have 50 green triangles?

- How many triangles do you need to make the largest triangle (with 50 green triangles)?

- What patterns did you notice as the triangles got larger?

- Do you think this is the same pattern we saw with the orange square? Explain your thinking. Do you think this pattern would be the same using other Pattern Blocks?

- Do you think you could predict the number of blocks needed to make the next larger triangle? Explain your answer.

JOURNAL REFLECTION

Why *do you think mathematicians call numbers such as 1, 4, 9, 16, and 25 square numbers?*

How many *green triangles do you think are needed to make the tenth triangle? Explain your answer.*

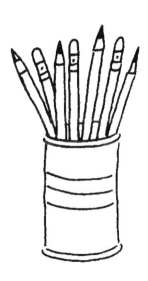

QUESTION 18

What is the average number?

Use 2 yellow hexagons, 1 red trapezoid, 1 blue rhombus, 3 green triangles, and 1 tan rhombus. What is the average number of sides? What blocks would you need to change for the average number of sides to be 5? Make a recording of your work. Explain how you decided what blocks to use for finding an average of 5 sides.

MATERIALS

For each pair of students

- Pattern Blocks
- paper, pencils, and crayons for recording

For the overhead projector

- Pattern Blocks

INTRODUCING THE QUESTION

1 Show the following blocks on the overhead projector: I green triangle, I blue rhombus, I red trapezoid, and I orange square. **What is the average number of sides for these blocks?** (4)

2 Encourage students to make deductions by looking at the blocks rather than by solving with pencil and paper. **I'm not looking for the exact average, but** *about* **the average number of sides. Which number of sides are there the most of?** (4)

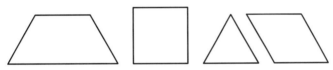

3 Introduce the question. **Here's another problem that's a little more difficult. Use 2 yellow hexagons, I red trapezoid, I blue rhombus, 3 green triangles, and I tan rhombus. What is the average number of sides?** (4)

4 After students have figured this average, give them their next challenge. **What block(s) would you need to change for the average number of sides to be 5? Explain how you decided what blocks you would change.**

WHAT SHOULD YOU DO IF . . .

▶ Some students are not convinced that the average number of sides is 4?

▶ Some students know the formula for finding averages and solve this very quickly?

It is important for students to understand *what they* are doing. Encourage them to explain average to you. **What do you think the average is? How are you figuring the average?**

Students who find the answer with "pencil and paper" often have a very different experience explaining why their answer is correct. Getting a right answer and understanding why it is right are two different things. Encourage students to "prove" their answers.

WHAT YOU MIGHT SEE

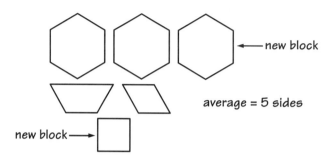

Some students may remove some of the original blocks and add new blocks to find an average of 5 sides.

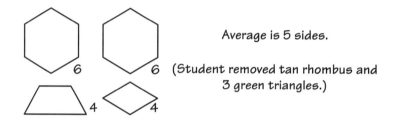

Some students may only add new blocks or remove original blocks to find an average of 5 sides.

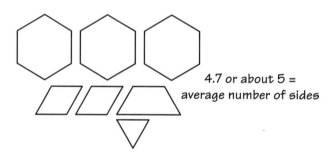

Some students may estimate the average to be 5 sides.

WHAT TO LOOK FOR IN STUDENT'S WORK

Was the student able to determine the average number of sides for the blocks given?

Was the student able to determine the blocks he would need to change for the average number of sides to be 5?

Does the student's explanation clearly state his thinking?

QUESTIONS FOR DISCUSSION

- What was the average number of sides for the blocks given? How did you figure the average?

- What blocks did you change for the average number of sides to be 5? How did you figure the average?

- Did anyone change the same blocks? Did you figure the average the same way or another way?

- Did anyone change different blocks for the average number of sides to be 5? What did you do?

JOURNAL REFLECTION

Do you think you could add blocks to the original blocks to make the average number of sides be 3? Why or why not?

Is this the way you have found averages before? If it is different, explain which way you think is better.

QUESTION 19

How many blue blocks would you need?

How many blue rhombuses would you need to cover a shape made with 50 red trapezoids? Use your Pattern Blocks to help you find the answer. Then record your work and explain how you know the number of blue blocks you would need.

MATERIALS

For each pair of students

■ Pattern Blocks (blue and red)
■ paper, pencils, and crayons for recording

For the overhead projector

■ Pattern Blocks

INTRODUCING THE QUESTION

1 Show a red trapezoid on the overhead projector. **How many green triangles do you need to cover this shape?** (3) Cover the trapezoid with the 3 green triangles.

2 **If there were 4 trapezoids, how many green triangles would you need to cover them?** (12) **How do you know?** Have students give their solutions and explanations.

3 Introduce the question to the class. **Use your Pattern Blocks. How many blue rhombuses would you need to cover a shape made with 50 red trapezoids? Record your work and explain how you know the number of blue blocks you would need.**

WHAT SHOULD YOU DO IF . . .

▶ Some students think they must know what the shape made with 50 red trapezoids looks like?

▶ Some students are trying to solve the question using blocks other than the blue and red blocks?

Some students may need a concrete representation to "see" the shape. Since it is unlikely the students will have 50 red trapezoids to make the shape, encourage students to find alternative ways to create a shape with their limited resources.

How interesting! Some students may think of a strategy so completely different that we think it couldn't possibly work. Try not to interfere—the students should decide when to abandon a strategy. Different strategies will add to your class discussion.

WHAT YOU MIGHT SEE

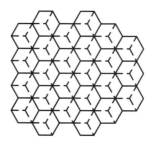

Some students may make 25 hexagons with the trapezoids and cover the hexagon shape with 3 rhombuses to determine there would be 75 blue blocks.

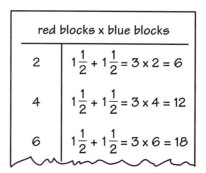

1 red = $1\frac{1}{2}$ blue blocks

red blocks x blue blocks	
2	$1\frac{1}{2} + 1\frac{1}{2} = 3 \times 2 = 6$
4	$1\frac{1}{2} + 1\frac{1}{2} = 3 \times 4 = 12$
6	$1\frac{1}{2} + 1\frac{1}{2} = 3 \times 6 = 18$

Some students may determine it takes $1\frac{1}{2}$ rhombuses to make a trapezoid. They may find the solution using this information.

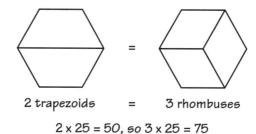

2 trapezoids = 3 rhombuses

$2 \times 25 = 50$, so $3 \times 25 = 75$

Some students may find the solution by recognizing a 2 to 3 ratio between the blocks.

WHAT TO LOOK FOR IN STUDENT'S WORK

Was the student able to determine that it takes 75 blue rhombuses to cover 50 red trapezoids?

Was the student able to explain clearly the strategy she used for solving the question?

QUESTIONS FOR DISCUSSION

- How many blue rhombuses do you think you would need to cover 50 trapezoids? How do you know?

- Did anyone come up with another number?

- Did anyone use a different strategy for finding the number of blue rhombuses it takes to cover 50 red trapezoids?

- Do you think the number of blue blocks you would need to cover a shape made of 50 red blocks would be different, depending on the shape? Why or why not?

JOURNAL REFLECTION

Explain the way someone else solved this question. It should not be the same strategy you used. Do you think they had a good strategy? Why or why not?

Do you think it would be easier or more difficult to find the number of green blocks it takes to cover 50 trapezoids? Explain your thinking.

20

What does a design that is 20% blue look like?

Can you create a design where 20% of the area is blue? Use your Pattern Blocks to make a design. Then record your design and explain how you know 20% is blue.

MATERIALS

For each pair of students

■ Pattern Blocks

■ paper, pencils, and crayons for recording

For the overhead projector

■ Pattern Blocks

INTRODUCING THE QUESTION

1   On the overhead projector, show a blue rhombus. **If this rhombus has a value of 25%, how many do you need to make 100%?** (4) **How do you know?** Have students share their explanations. Place 4 blue rhombuses on the overhead to show 100%.

2   Remove 1 of the 4 blue rhombuses and add 2 green triangles. **What percentage of this design is blue?** (75%) **What percentage is green?** (25%) **How do you know?**

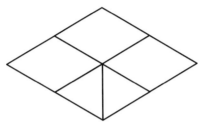

3   Introduce today's question. **With your partner, use your Pattern Blocks to create a design that is 20% blue. What does a design that is 20% blue look like? Record your work and explain how you know 20% of the design is blue.**

WHAT SHOULD YOU DO IF . . .

▶ Some students create a design that is greater than or less than 20% blue?

These students may have miscalculated the value of the blocks used in the design or they may need to review the concept of percentage. Have students explain their calculations to clarify any misconceptions.

▶ Some students quickly find a solution using 1 blue and 8 green Pattern Blocks?

Challenge these students to use other combinations of blocks. Can you create a design that is 20% blue using other Pattern Blocks in your set? How many different designs can you make?

WHAT YOU MIGHT SEE

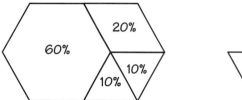 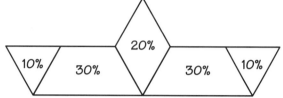

Some students may create designs that are 20% blue and label the value for each block.

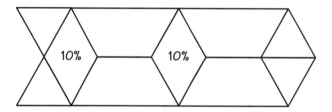

Some students may create a design that is 20% blue, identifying only the value of each blue block.

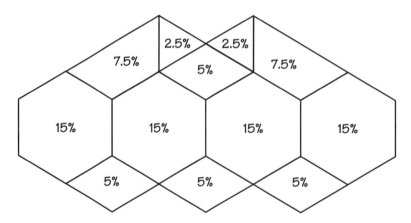

Some students may create large, complex designs where 20% is blue.

WHAT TO LOOK FOR IN STUDENT'S WORK

Was the student able to create a design that is 20% blue?

Did the student's explanation clearly state how he figured the percentages for the design?

Does the student's work indicate an understanding of percentages?

QUESTIONS FOR DISCUSSION

- What does your design that is 20% blue look like? How did you figure the value of the blocks?

- Did anyone create a different design? How did you figure the value of your blocks?

- Did anyone find the percentage of the blocks that were not blue? How did you figure their value?

- How did you decide which Pattern Blocks to use?

- Which Pattern Blocks do you notice being used the most? Why do you think so?

- How many blocks did you use to create your design? Did anyone create a design with more or fewer blocks?

- Does the number of blocks in the design affect how you figure the percentages? Do the Pattern Blocks always have the same value?

JOURNAL REFLECTION

How are percentages like fractions?

Can you create a design that is totally blue and answer today's question? Why or why not?

Did everyone's Pattern Blocks have the same value? Why do you think that is so?

1-INCH GRID PAPER

1-INCH GRID PAPER

TRIANGLE GRID PAPER

SPACESHIP

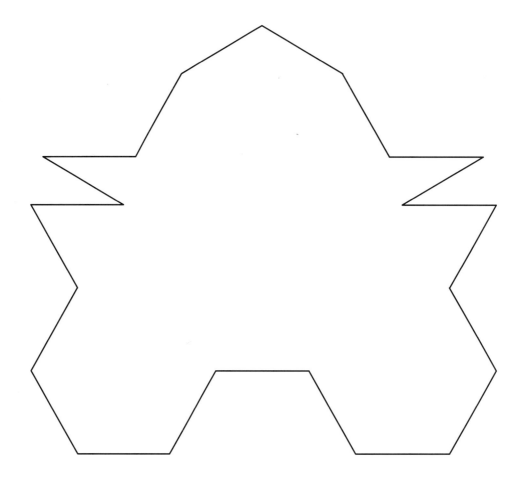

SPACESHIP REPRODUCIBLE